Mystery on the Rancho Grande

Mystery
on the
Rancho Grande

BY

Julia Bristol Bischoff

drawings by *MARTIN CHARLOT*

M

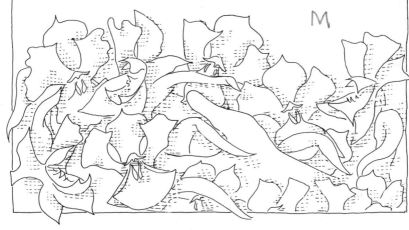

NEW YORK • YOUNG SCOTT BOOKS

Library of Congress Catalog Card No. 77–82266.
Text © 1969 by Julia Bristol Bischoff.
Illustrations © 1969 by Martin Charlot.
All rights reserved. Printed in U.S.A.

Contents

THE UNITED

DALLAS

MEXICO

NUEVO LAREDO

MONTERREY

SAN LUIS POTOSÍ

MEXICO CITY

OAXACA

N
W · E
S

TAMARA'S TRIP
DALLAS TO SAN ISIDRO

1. Call to Adventure

I was starving when I got home. I'd stopped at my friend Evelyn Miller's to play badminton.

Mother always has dinner ready by five-thirty—when Daddy comes home from work. He is an airplane mechanic at an "executive" airport. That's where small, private planes come in.

But tonight there wasn't a sign of dinner. At least, not on the table. Mother was sitting in the living room, cross-stitching on the front of a dress she was making for me.

"What's with dinner?" I asked.

"Your father is going to be late tonight."

I knew from the way she said it that something was up. "How late?" I asked.

"I think we can expect him by six-thirty or seven."

"Do we have to wait till then?"

I should have known better than ask that. Mother would never eat without Daddy even if she had to wait until midnight.

"If you're very hungry you can get yourself a glass of milk and a cookie or something," she said.

I hurried to the kitchen, where I made myself a fat cream-cheese-and-jelly sandwich and poured out a tall glass of milk.

"Why is Dad coming home so late?" I asked, after I'd carried them to the living room and curled up on the couch.

"Now, I don't want you to get all excited," she began.

This almost made me laugh, because whenever Mother says not to get excited it means she's all worked up about something herself. You see, my mother's a Latin—from Costa Rica. And, well, maybe all Latins get excited easily.

"Excited about what?" I asked.

"Yesterday your father worked on an airplane that belongs to a man named Rupert Ainsley. You've heard your Daddy speak of him, haven't you?"

"I don't remember. Who is he?"

Call to Adventure

"He has a ranch out in West Texas, not far from where your father was born. Some years ago they discovered oil on it. He's a millionaire now. He owns a hotel and lots of other property in Dallas. And not long ago he bought a big ranch in Costa Rica."

I nearly choked. I was beginning to get the picture. "And so—?"

"He and Wally hadn't seen each other since they were together in grade school. They got to talking and—well, he asked Wally to come to his hotel after work tonight to talk about taking a job on his ranch in Costa Rica."

"Mother!" I screamed. I understood now why she was so excited.

"Of course, he hasn't got the job yet," she said. "They are just going to talk. So we mustn't jump to any delusions."

She meant conclusions, of course. She speaks English almost perfectly with only a tiny bit of accent. But every now and then, especially if she's upset or anything, she uses a wrong word.

"It—it's fifteen years since I saw my country," she said, and from the sound of her voice I thought maybe she was going to cry.

You see, my Dad, Wally Perkins, used to be in the Marines. And once when his ship docked at Long Beach, California, he met my mother. She was a Costa Rican school teacher who was staying with some friends in Los Angeles and studying English. She's of Spanish descent and has dark hair and eyes, though her skin is like ivory. And well, they fell in love and got married. That was fourteen years ago. I'm their only child and I'm twelve. My name is Tamara. Tamara Perkins.

Mother had always been a little homesick for her Costa Rica. Of course, she could have gone back for a visit any time. The trouble was we never had enough money so we could all fly down together, and Daddy couldn't take off from work long enough so we could go so far by boat. And she wouldn't think of going without him.

I can remember when I was little hearing her and Daddy talk—after they put me to bed—about moving down to Costa Rica. But Daddy was always afraid he couldn't make a good enough living there. So maybe you can imagine how the idea of his getting a good job and our moving to a Costa Rican ranch had us walking on air.

"Do you really think we might go?" I wondered out loud.

"We'll have to see what your father says when he comes." She put her sewing away and got up. "It's time now for me to start supper. When you finish eating your snack you can set the table."

Call to Adventure

It seemed a thousand years before Daddy arrived. And all that time I couldn't get another word out of Mother. When Dad did get home he kissed her as usual, sat down at the table and started to eat as though this were a day like any other day.

Daddy is tall and lanky, with sandy hair and freckled skin. (I got my red hair from my Grandmother Perkins.) He likes to make out he never gets excited about anything, but he doesn't fool me. Underneath he's just as excitable as Mother. After a while, Mother couldn't stand it any longer either. "Come on, Wally, tell us all about it," she coaxed, when he had eaten enough to take the edge off his appetite.

"Well," Daddy began, "it seems Rupert Ainsley has a ten-thousand-acre ranch in Costa Rica. About every three months he flies down in his plane to see how things are going. But apparently they aren't going very well. For instance, he's shipped down a lot of machinery: tractors, trucks, power saws, electric motors, and I don't know what all. But every time he goes down he finds most of the machinery out of order. No one ever seems able to fix anything." Dad stopped to eat some more.

"Is that what he wants you for—to fix the machinery?" Mother asked. "Or would you be running the ranch?"

"He has a foreman, a Costa Rican fellow named Gomez, who has been running the ranch for quite a while. I'd have to work under him, but I'd be assistant foreman, as well as chief mechanic."

You see, before Daddy went in the Marines he had been a foreman on a ranch in western Texas. After he got out of the service and married my mother, he went back to his old job on the ranch there, but Mother didn't like that part of Texas very well. "It's so flat," she would say. She was used to mountains, and she missed them. "It's too cold in winter and too hot in summer," she would continue. In San José, the capital of Costa Rica where she grew up, it was never very hot or very cold. Always just about right, she said.

Anyhow, when I was nine we moved to Dallas and Dad started working as an airplane mechanic. It was a trade he had learned while in the Marines; they have airplanes in the Marines, too, you know. Actually he can fix just about anything: farm machinery, radios, refrigerators, automobiles—well, you name it.

Dad had thought that maybe since Mother had lived most of her life in a city, she might feel more at home in Dallas. And I guess she did—a little. The trouble was that Daddy wasn't so happy. He didn't like the noise and smog and traffic and hurry-hurry. He really loves those wide open spaces.

"Whereabouts in Costa Rica is Mr. Ainsley's ranch?" Mother finally asked. "Did he tell you?"

14

Call to Adventure

"It's in a valley—" Dad scratched his head, trying to remember. "The General Valley, it seems to me he said—wherever that is."

Mother looked puzzled for a minute. Then she said, "You don't mean the *Valle de El General?*" She pronounced General as though it was *Hen-er-al,* because that's the way you pronounce the *g* in Spanish. And she put an accent on the last syllable.

"Yes, that's it, I think," Dad said.

"But that's on the other side of the Talamancas!" From Mother's tone you might think she meant on the far side of the moon.

"Yes. The Talamanca Mountains. I remember now. Have you ever been in that part of Costa Rica?"

"Good heavens, no!" Mother exclaimed.

"Why do you say it like that?" I put in.

She hesitated for a moment, and then said, "When I was a girl in Costa Rica, there was hardly anyone living in the General Valley, except maybe a few Indians. There was nothing there but forests and jungles, full of all sorts of wild animals: jaguars, pumas, tapirs, monkeys, wild pigs . . . . There were hardly any roads. The truth is, it wasn't considered very nice to live anywhere except up on the *Meseta Central.* That's the central highland around San José. To live off the *Meseta* was a little like living on the wrong side of the tracks in an

15

American city. But of course it's fifteen years since I left my country."

"Since then they've built a highway all the way down through there," Dad said. "And according to Ainsley, people are moving in quite rapidly now—including a few North Americans. Still, I get the impression that this is raw, new territory, just opening up. A real frontier —Latin-American style."

"Oh boy," I said. "It sounds like when the pioneers went West, over the Rocky Mountains. Will there be shooting and cattle rustling, with two-gun sheriffs chasing bad men, like in the movies?" I had goose pimples just thinking about it.

Mother laughed. "Nothing like that, I'm sure. My people are noted for their friendliness, and they are the most peace-loving people in the world. Why, Costa Rica doesn't even have a regular army."

"You mean there aren't any bad people at all in Costa Rica?" I said. Mother would never admit there was anything wrong with her dear Costa Rica.

"I wouldn't say that," she said. "There are some bad people everywhere."

I ran around the table and kissed her. "I was just teasing," I said.

"I knew you were."

"What I wonder," Dad said, "is how it happens that a

16

little country like Costa Rica has so much unused land?"

"We're not so little," Mother answered quickly. "Costa Rica is twice as big as Holland, but has only about a tenth as many people. We're one of the few countries in the world with land to spare."

"Of course," Dad continued, "the sensible thing would be to go down and look over the situation first. But I couldn't take that much time off from my job, without quitting."

"It's taking a chance, of course, to go so far to a new job when you know so little about the country and the men you would be working with," Mother agreed.

"You have to take some chances in this life, though," said Dad. "If I learned anything in the Marines it was that."

They talked on and *on* and ON. All the while I was fairly holding my breath.

Mr. Ainsley wouldn't pay Dad quite as much as he was making at the airport, but he would provide a house so we wouldn't have any rent to pay. We'd have free electricity, too. He wanted an answer right away, though; otherwise he'd have to look for someone else.

Finally Dad said, "It's up to you, Lisa. Ainsley says his place is thirty miles from the nearest town of any size. Maybe it's too wild for you? I wouldn't want you to feel you're living on the wrong side of the tracks."

17

"No, it's up to you, Wally. You make the decision."

They were driving me mad with their hemming and hawing.

"There is one thing I should tell you before you make up your mind," Dad said. "Mr. Ainsley admits he's sent down five other mechanics or assistant foremen in the past three years and none of them stayed more than three or four months. We can't afford to pull up stakes and move so far away unless we're sure of staying at least a couple of years."

"Naturally not," Mother agreed.

"But he thought since my wife is a Costa Rican, I might get along better than any of the others." Dad grinned.

"I'm glad if your Costa Rican wife is of some value to you," Mother laughed.

"Well, what do you say, Lisa?"

Mother took so long answering that I felt like jumping up and down and screaming, "Say you'll go, Mother. Please, *please,* say you'll go."

At last she said, "I think this must be the answer to all my prayers. I know we'll all love it."

"Okay, then, it's settled," Dad said.

The thought of moving to a strange new land—one I'd been hearing about all my life—left me tingling from head to foot.

2. Our Covered Wagon

Dad talked with Mr. Ainsley again the next day, and it was decided that the best way for us to get to Costa Rica would be to drive down on the Inter-American highway.

"What's that?" I asked.

"That's a road, built partly by our United States government, that goes all the way down through Mexico and Central America to the Panama Canal. It passes right by Ainsley's ranch. Here, Ainsley gave me this map."

Dad unfolded a big map of Mexico and Central America and spread it out on our dining table. A bright red line showed where the road ran.

19

Mystery on the Rancho Grande

"Aren't there some bridges missing, or something, on that road?" Mother asked.

"There were, but all the bridges are in now, Ainsley says. And there's a smooth new paved section through Guatemala in place of a terrible road that was used before," Dad said. "About the only part left that isn't hard surfaced is a stretch between San José and the border of Panama."

"They were just beginning to build the highway when I left Costa Rica," Mother said.

"How did you get to the United States?" I asked. She'd probably told me before, but it hadn't meant anything then.

"I went from San José to Puntarenas by train"—she showed me on the map where that Pacific port was— "and took a boat from there to California."

Later Mother asked, "What about our household things? Can we ship them?"

"There's no way, Ainsley says—at least, no way that wouldn't cost more than the stuff is worth," Dad replied. "But I can get a small trailer to haul the things we must take. We'll have to sell most of the furniture. Do you think you could be ready to go by December twenty-eighth?"

Mother studied the calendar on the wall. "Let's see, that would give us about two weeks and a half—."

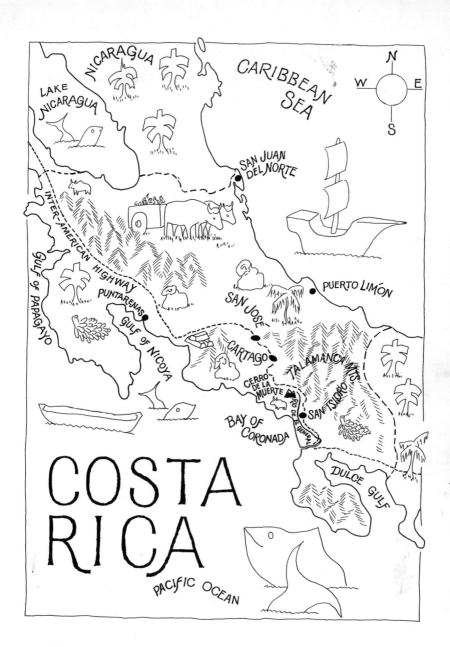

COSTA RICA

"Ainsley would like me to be there by the middle of January," Dad said. "I thought if we started on the twenty-eighth we'd be over the border in time to miss the New Year's traffic, and could easily make it by the fifteenth or sixteenth of the month."

"I think I can manage," Mother said.

Well, you never saw busier people than we were. It gets dark early, of course, in December. But Dad put all the lights on in the garage and worked until ten or eleven o'clock every night on what he jokingly called our "covered wagon."

Just before we moved to Dallas, Dad had bought a pickup truck, and he had never turned it in for another car. It used to bother me that we didn't have a regular car like other people, but now it turned out to be just the thing. Dad bought a secondhand camper that fit onto the back of the pickup, and then he started fixing it up. There was a place for Mom and Dad to sleep, and up above the cab, a place for me. Their beds could be pushed up out of the way during the daytime, and there was a little table you could pull out, and folding stools and a camp stove with two burners. And we got a styrofoam icebox to keep our food in.

Dad worked very hard getting everything ready in time. I guess he sometimes wished that I was a boy so I could help him more, but he managed to keep me

22

pretty busy anyway: running errands, fetching things, and doing all sorts of small chores.

We had so much to do. Mother and Dad had to get passports, and we all had to have passport pictures made. You can't just barge into foreign countries, you know. After you get passports, you have to get visas from the consuls of all the countries you'll be going through. But Mother said, "I don't know if all the countries have consulates here in Dallas. Why don't we just get visas for Mexico now. Then we can get the rest in Mexico City. That will give us a chance to see the city." Daddy thought this a good idea too, and that's what we decided to do.

Meanwhile Daddy and I both began working like mad on our Spanish. Ever since I could remember, Mother had been trying to teach us Spanish. We were sorry now we hadn't been better pupils. Often when Mother spoke to us in Spanish we'd answer in English because it was easier and we were just plain lazy. But from the day we knew we were going to Costa Rica, Mother began speaking Spanish to us all the time. And if we answered her in English she'd pretend she didn't understand us, so we'd have to repeat it in Spanish. Daddy spoke quite well, but I still needed to learn a lot more.

Then, on top of everything else, there was Christmas.

Luckily Mother had most of her gift shopping done and so did I. But there were lots of other things to buy. We all got boots and extra pairs of shoes and dungarees and all sorts of little things like toothbrushes and thread and band-aids.

"It's not that you can't buy all these things in Costa Rica," Mother explained, "but if the ranch is thirty miles from the nearest town of any size, it will be better to have plenty of supplies on hand."

One day while Mother and I were shopping in downtown Dallas, she took me to a bookstore and we bought a guidebook to Mexico and Central America.

"Don't think you're going to sight-see all the way down to Costa Rica," Dad said when he saw it. "We'll have enough to do, driving that many miles in a little over two weeks, without rubbernecking on the way."

"Don't worry," Mother said, "we just got the book so we could learn what we'll be missing by not stopping anywhere."

At this both she and Dad burst out laughing, because Mother has her little ways of getting around him. In the end it was decided we could pick out one or two things to see in each country that wouldn't take us too much out of the way. But the more we studied the guidebook, the harder it was to decide where we wanted to go most. There seemed to be so many marvelous things we shouldn't miss seeing in that part of the world.

Daddy gave notice where he worked that he was quitting as of the Friday before Christmas. And a few days before our Christmas vacation, Mother went to see the principal of my school to explain why I wouldn't be coming back after the holidays. I was in the seventh grade, and Mother found out how I could finish the grade by correspondence.

Well, you should have heard the questions the kids fired at me during recess. I mean, after the teacher announced to the whole school that I wouldn't be back after our vacation because my folks were moving to Costa Rica.

"Where is Costa Rica?"

"You mean you're going to live on an island?"

"How do you think you'll like living with all those Puerto Ricans?"

"Won't it be awfully hot down there?"

Before they got through asking questions, I decided that practically nobody knows where Costa Rica is. Oh, most know better than to mix it up with the island of Puerto Rico, and quite a few know it's somewhere in Central America. But if you can find one person in ten who can tell you it's located in Central America between Nicaragua and Panama—well, all I can say is, your friends are a lot better at geography than mine are.

Mystery on the Rancho Grande

We didn't have much time for Christmas this year. Dad had put a sign out in front of our house, FURNI- TURE FOR SALE, and there were all kinds of people coming in and out to look at things. And there were packing boxes all over the place. We were so excited about our trip, though, that Christmas didn't seem as important as in other years. We had bought so many things to take with us that we hardly knew which were presents and which were simply things we needed.

The day after Christmas, Evelyn invited me over to her house for the afternoon. I didn't think Mother would let me go; we were so busy. But to my surprise she did.

Afterwards I understood. Mother knew all the time that Evelyn was planning a surprise farewell party for me. I nearly jumped out of my skin when I walked into the living room and my friends popped up from behind furniture and doors, all yelling "Boo!" at the same time. There were eighteen kids altogether, mostly from my class in school.

It was a lovely party. Their house was decorated for Christmas, and Mrs. Miller served us fruitcake and ice cream and some delicious punch. The kids had chipped in and bought me a red plaid carrying case, with a red lining and a mirror inside the cover.

On our last night in Dallas, we had to sleep in our camper. It was comical, sleeping in our garage in the

Our Covered Wagon

car. But we had to, because all our furniture had been
sold except for things we were taking with us, and Dad
had already packed that stuff in the car and trailer so
we'd be ready to get away early in the morning. We
didn't keep much except personal things, like clothes
and books and records and a portable player and dishes
and bedding. And, of course, our refrigerator and washing machine and sewing machine, because, Mother said,
electrical appliances cost an awful lot in most foreign
countries.

In the morning Mother made breakfast on our camp
stove—just as though we were already on the road—
since the gas and electricity in the house had been
turned off.

Evelyn came over early, with another of my girl
friends, Mary Kirby, to say good-bye. They could hardly
believe how much stuff Dad had managed to pack into
our car and trailer. We were really jammed in.

I know my heart was beating double time when we
finally pulled out of our driveway, with the girls waving good-bye. I was so happy it seemed as though I'd
burst, and yet I was crying, too! I'll never forget my last
look at our little pink stucco house—Daddy had never
gotten the grass to grow around it very well. Then the
tears in my eyes made it all blurry, like a smeared
painting.

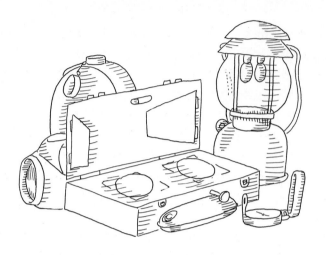

3. New Year's in Mexico

The first day we drove almost to Laredo, which is four hundred miles from Dallas. When it started to get dark we found a roadside camp where we could stop for the night. Mother opened some cans and fixed supper. Then after I'd washed our few dishes under a nearby pump we piled into our camper beds.

Early next morning we drove through the town of Laredo that I'd heard so much about in Western songs and movies, then across the bridge over the Rio Grande River that separates the United States from Mexico.

At the end of the bridge there was a Mexican cus-tomshouse. When you cross a border into a different country, I learned, you always have to show your passport to the customs officials. Then they look over your baggage to see if you're bringing into their country anything that's against their laws.

We had so much stuff that it seemed to take forever for the officials to pull out everything and look through it. To keep from biting my fingernails I walked back a short distance onto the bridge and looked down at the Rio Grande.

What a letdown that was! From the maps you'd think it was a real big river. Instead, there was nothing but a trickle of muddy water flowing with the speed of molasses over a sandy bed. But Mother said that sometimes, after a lot of rain, the water is very high. And once in a while there are terrible floods when it overflows its banks.

At last, after Daddy had put everything back in our car and trailer, we were on our way—traveling through a foreign land. The Inter-American highway begins at Nuevo Laredo, the Mexican town on the other side of the Rio Grande from our Laredo.

The northern part of Mexico is a desert, with not much growing in it but cactus. There are some people living there, though. Since they don't have trees to give them wood, they build their houses out of a kind of mud bricks called adobe. A few were whitewashed, but most of them simply had been left the mud color of the bricks. They were small and had dirt floors and tiny windows.

This desert part of Mexico is quite flat. But much of the time we were going gradually uphill, and pretty soon we began to see mountains. The first big town we came to was Monterrey. There we got on a wonderful new stretch of road that climbed up and up until we arrived at a town called Saltillo, which means "Little Waterfall." Getting through the town you cross the same rushing, winding, mountain stream five times!

In Saltillo most of the houses were covered with stucco, painted white, and they came right out to the sidewalk, with no front yards at all.

"The yards are in back of the houses and surrounded by high walls," Mother explained. "They are called *patios*, but they're a lot more enclosed than what people in the States usually call patios."

The main highways in Mexico are very good. The only trouble is you have to keep on the lookout for animals—cows, goats, chickens, mules—that are always wandering out on them. Anyhow, by nightfall we were nearly halfway to Mexico City. We hadn't seen any roadside camping places, but when it started to get dark Dad just pulled off the road. Nobody seemed to mind if you stopped anywhere you wanted to.

New Year's in Mexico

The next day we really began to see mountains. Living all my life in the flat part of Texas, you can imagine how thrilled I was to see all the mountains and lovely valleys. Everywhere there seemed to be flowers. Mexico, I decided, is really the land of flowers.

Some of the new Mexican highways, like the one we were on, go around the larger cities—just like in the United States. But Mother got Daddy to turn off at the town of San Luis Potosí so we could go to the market and buy some oranges and bananas and other things. Dad stopped beside a park that was full of flowers and surrounded by several big old churches. He stayed in the car to keep an eye on all our belongings while Mother and I walked over cobblestoned streets until we found the marketplace.

Nearly all the people selling things were Indians. And you can hardly imagine how beautiful and colorful the market was, with all the fruits and vegetables laid out on mats in neat little piles.

We didn't stop again until we got to Mexico City. There we found a very nice parklike place just outside the city where we could camp. There were quite a few other Americans around, in all sorts of campers and house trailers.

One couple, when they saw our Texas license plates, came over to talk to us. It was a good thing they did, too. When we told them we were going into the city the next day, they advised us to leave our car and take the bus in. The traffic in Mexico City, they said, was awfully heavy, and it was even harder to find a place to park than in downtown Austin, which was where they came from.

The next morning we took a bus into the city. And what a city! Did you know that Mexico City has six million people? But it's beautiful. There are lots of parks, even right down near the center of town. One of the streets is so wide that it has four separate rows of trees growing along it, and every three or four blocks there's a small park right in the middle of the intersection, with flowers and fountains and statues in it. Also benches to sit on.

And, can you imagine, we had to wear sweaters or coats the whole time we were there. That's one of the things you learn when you start traveling south. It's not nearly as hot as most people believe. It all depends on how high you are. Mexico City is over 7,000 feet high, so it's cool there all the time. Mother says it's only in the lowlands that it gets really hot in the tropics, and even there it's seldom as hot as it gets sometimes during summer in Texas.

Well, it was a job going around to the consulates, and soon we saw that it wouldn't be possible for us to get visas for all five of the Central American countries in a single day. Although the consulates were all quite near together, it always took us quite a while to find our way from one to the other. Then, in each place, we'd have to wait and fill out a lot of papers, then wait some more. Besides, we discovered, the consulates were closing early because this was New Year's Eve. What's more, New Year's Day fell on a Saturday, so they wouldn't be open again until Monday!

Daddy had been so busy getting ready to leave that he hadn't thought about offices being closed when we arrived in Mexico City.

"Can't we get the rest of the visas in some town along the way?" he asked.

"I doubt if they have consulates in small towns," Mother said.

"Can't we go on to Guatemala and get the rest in the capital there?"

Mother bit her lip. "The trouble is we don't have the one for Guatemala."

I think Dad would have hit the ceiling then if there'd been one above the park bench where we were sitting. "Why on earth didn't we get that one first?"

"I don't know," Mother replied. "I suppose because we didn't realize we couldn't get them all today."

Poor Daddy was fuming. "After hurrying like mad for

three weeks, now we have to sit here doing nothing for two whole days."

Without realizing it, they had forgotten their pact and were both speaking English.

It took quite a few minutes for Mother to soothe him down. "I know how you feel," she said, "but it will be a wonderful experience to spend New Year's in Mexico City. Something Tamara will never forget. And it will do you good to relax a little. We have time, I'm sure, to reach the ranch by the fifteenth."

"Providing we don't have any car trouble," Dad grumbled.

From the way Mother glanced at me out of the corner of her eye while she was calming Daddy down, I had a hunch she'd known all along that we would arrive in Mexico City right at New Year's. Anyhow, I'm sure that afterwards Daddy was glad it had turned out that way, too.

Now that it was too late to visit any more consulates, we started walking around to see some more of the city. Mother had the guidebook in her purse, and after studying it for a while, we decided to visit a part of the city called the Zócalo. This is a big square with an immense cathedral on one side and long government buildings around the other sides. It was here, according to the guidebook, that the palace of the great Indian chief,

New Year's in Mexico

Montezuma, stood when the Spaniards first came to Mexico over four hundred years ago.

After we got back to our camp, the people from Austin asked us over to their trailer for the evening. They had also invited a family from California, and we had a regular party that lasted until we welcomed in the New Year—1966.

We spent most of the next day in a park called Chapultepec, which has lagoons and fountains and birds and miles of gorgeous flower beds. It's so big you can hardly see it all in one day. High on a hill in the middle of it is an enormous castle where an emperor and empress once lived—the first real castle I ever saw. It has I-don't-know-how-many rooms. And in one part, you can still see the fancy, gold-trimmed royal coach the emperor and empress traveled in.

The next day Mother packed some lunch and we went to a place called Xochimilco. "It was once a lake," Mother explained, after consulting the guidebook. "The Indians who lived around it used to make flower gardens on rafts—floating gardens, they were called. They'd paddle them around to the houses on the edge of the lake to sell their flowers. Sometimes, when rafts were abandoned, they would take root and gradually form little islands."

There were boats decorated with flowers and banners

that you could rent, and the boatman would paddle you all around the waterways between the islands. Daddy rented a pretty one, red with a blue-and-white-striped awning over it and fresh flowers around the top. There were hundreds of boats on the waterways. Lots of the people were playing guitars or accordions, and everybody was singing and eating their picnic lunches, including us. It was one of the most marvelous days I ever spent.

It was noon the next day by the time we got our last two visas and left Mexico City. There are several roads you can take to get out of the city. Mother held the map and acted as navigator. She managed to direct Dad to a road where we could see a mountain peak so high that even though it's in the tropics, it has snow on it all year around. It has an Indian name—Popocatépetl.

There are mountains all through the southern part of Mexico. But after we passed Oaxaca we really got into mountains. The country here was dry and brown and stony. We saw hardly any traffic except for a few big trucks and once in a while a jeep.

The road went up and down and wound around so much that I nearly got dizzy. Sometimes we went around a curve with a high cliff on one side and a ravine so deep on the other that we couldn't even see the bottom. The road was little more than a shelf hewn out of the mountainside, with no railings around the dangerous places. I guess they expect you to drive carefully or else! I was glad Dad is such a good driver.

One thing amused us, though. Sometimes after the road had been twisting and turning for miles, there was an arrow pointing ahead with the words on it, *"Camino sinuoso."* That's Spanish for "winding road." We laughed each time we saw one of these signs because we didn't see how any road could be any more *"sinuoso"* than what we'd already been driving over.

Finally, on our third day out from Mexico City, we got down to the Isthmus of Tehuantepec. It was very warm there, because now we were down near sea level. There were banana and palm trees growing everywhere and flowering trees and plants that I'd never seen before. And the most terrific birds: brilliantly colored jays and parrots and toucans—those birds with beaks nearly as long as they are.

In the town of Tehuantepec, when we stopped for gas, we saw lots of Indian women. Most of them were barefooted, and they wore bright-colored skirts that came to their ankles, with wide ruffles around the bottom, and fancy embroidered blouses. They were tall and straight, and if they had anything to carry, they carried it balanced on their heads.

Off to the right, we could see the blue of what we

thought must be the Pacific Ocean. It was my first glimpse of an ocean, and I was dying to go down and camp on the shore. But after Daddy studied the map for a while, he decided that we were probably seeing inlets or bays. "They might be surrounded by marshes," he said. "Regular mosquito resorts."

Farther on, there was a stretch of road that crossed a lot of small rivers, and we found a nice place beside one of them where we could bathe and camp for the night. Before going to bed we had another look at our map— by lantern light. We had already been traveling for nine days just driving through Mexico. And we still had four Central American countries to cross before we got to Costa Rica.

4. Where the Pigs Wear Shoes

By eight o'clock next morning we had reached the border of Guatemala—the beginning of Central America.

We had thought the officials in Mexico were pokey, but then we hadn't met the ones in Guatemala. They were ever so polite, but they not only took everything out of the car, they looked under the seat cushions, under the fenders, and even behind the license plate.

They kept asking if we had any guns. Dad said later, "I guess they're having some trouble with bandits who hide out in the hills, and they don't want anyone to bring in guns that they could get hold of."

At last we were on our way again—winding up into

more mountain country. A lot of Indians live in this part of Central America, and you should see their costumes! The people of each town dress differently, especially the men. We saw some men wearing short tunics like page boys in olden times. Others had on red-and-white-striped trousers or baggy bright red and blue pants. And most of them were wearing straw hats with ribbons on them; some had long streamers like on little girls' hats.

The people of Guatemala use donkeys a lot. The ones we saw were small and shaggy, with big, soulful eyes. I would have given almost anything to buy one and take it along, but Dad said, "I couldn't squeeze another toothpick into this car, let alone a donkey."

It was starting to get dark when we neared Guatemala City, the capital of Guatemala. Suddenly we looked down from the top of an encircling ridge of hills and there was the city, spread out below us in a saucer-like valley. It was like something out of a fairy tale.

Daddy stopped the car, and we watched as the shadows of the mountain peaks crept in over the city. Then the lights in all the thousands of homes came on, sparkling like diamonds in the clear, cool highland air.

"All through the mountain chain that extends from the United States down through Mexico and Central and South America there are cities and towns like this one, set in high mountain valleys," said Mother. "The air in them is so wonderful that they're sometimes called the 'air-conditioned' cities of Latin America."

Dad needed to have the car checked over and greased, so we drove to a big service station that was near the center of town. They couldn't do the work until morning, but they said we could leave the car right on their big lot and sleep there. We found a restaurant not far away where we ate dinner and breakfast.

Next morning while the car was being serviced, Mother and I walked around, and found we weren't far from a big marketplace. What a market! It spread over a whole block. There were Indians in every sort of costume. Lots of Indian children, too. And just about every kind of fruit and vegetable you can think of. There were baskets and straw hats and jugs and blankets and hundreds more things. Oh, yes, and saddles! Which reminded me that I hoped to ride horseback when we got to the ranch. Besides a lot of different things to eat, Mother bought some hand-embroidered cloth for a dress for me and a skirt for herself.

Daddy hadn't come with us because he thought he had better stay and keep an eye on our things while the men were working on the car. When we got back, we told him we'd stay with the car while he walked around to the market.

Mystery on the Rancho Grande

"It's really worth seeing, and you missed the one in San Luis Potosí," Mother told him.

Well, Daddy went. He was gone quite a while, and when he came back, we had to laugh at what he had bought for himself. It was a machete—a kind of wide-bladed knife nearly two feet long. It had a leather case that you could fasten onto your belt, like an old-time sword.

"We used machetes in the Marines," Daddy said, "and ever since we crossed the border into Mexico, nearly every man I've seen has been wearing one."

"Every workman, you mean," Mother said.

"I don't think there's another tool in the world quite so handy," Daddy continued. "Here they seem to use them for everything: to clear ground and hoe, to cut hay and sugar cane, chop wood, even to peel fruit. Anyhow," Daddy grinned roguishly, "I thought if I'm going to live in Latin America, I should learn to do as Latins do. And I couldn't think of a better way to begin than by buying a machete."

Mother took the big knife, pulled it out of its leather sheath and examined the trademark. "Made in USA," she read.

"In Connecticut—where practically half the machetes in the world are made," Dad said.

"So you came to Guatemala to buy it," Mother

laughed. Then she added, "Anyhow, I'm sure it will come in handy."

After we left Guatemala City, we drove through miles and miles of coffee plantations. It was beautiful hilly country. Coffee trees—or maybe I should say bushes—can't stand much sun, so the farmers plant tall, scraggly trees to shade them. These shade trees are called *madres* (which means "mothers") because they are like mothers protecting the little coffee trees.

Most of the coffee had already been picked, but there were a few bright red berries still clinging to the bushes. Talk about Christmas trees! Coffee bushes have shiny, dark green leaves and are just a nice height. If you chopped one down while the berries were still on it, you'd have a perfect tree already trimmed—except no one would do that because they are too valuable.

After a while, the road was mostly downhill as we descended from the Guatemalan highlands and approached the border of El Salvador. The customs officials didn't take so long here; still, they looked us over pretty thoroughly, from passports to baggage.

El Salvador is lower and warmer than Guatemala. It has the most people for its size of any Latin-American country. Every inch of land seemed to be cultivated, and the whole landscape was like a lovely garden.

In the mountains off to our left, there were lots of

volcanoes. They look like upside-down ice-cream cones, except they are a blackish-gray color. This is because the lava they shoot out every now and then kills the trees and plants around them. None of them was erupting, which I suppose was lucky for the people of El Salvador, but I would have loved to see one in action.

Another thing I noticed about El Salvador was the size of the trees. They have trees that are two or three times as tall as most of our trees back home. You can hardly imagine how dramatic they look against the blue sky and the hazy mountains off in the distance.

I missed the donkeys, though—I didn't see a single one. Instead, there were oxen and oxcarts everywhere, on the roads and in the fields.

It was late afternoon when we passed through San Salvador, the capital of El Salvador, and people were just getting off from work. There were so many of them that the sidewalks wouldn't hold them all and they overflowed into the streets. We had to drive very slowly and wait for them to get out of the way. But this gave me a chance to look at everything. Most of the people were dressed just about the way we dress at home in summertime, only there weren't any women in shorts.

It was very built-up along the highway, with dozens of new-looking factories, and we began to wonder where we could stop for the night. We saw lots of little

46

stands along the way where people sold food. In some of them, women were cooking things on charcoal stoves. We were getting hungry, so Daddy stopped and Mother went up to a stand—with me tagging along, of course.

She bought a half-dozen tortilla cheese sandwiches. Tortillas, as you probably know, are flat, round pancakes made of ground fresh corn. These had melted cheese between them. Then, at another stand, we bought three huge green coconuts. The man who was selling them chopped the tops off for us—with a machete, of course—and gave us some straws so we could drink the juice from inside.

We parked under some big trees while we ate. The sandwiches were delicious, and I think each coconut held at least a pint of "milk." Coconuts that aren't completely ripe contain much more liquid than ripe ones. They're easier to open, too, because the outside hasn't turned to wood yet.

We weren't hungry any more, but we still needed to find a place to stop for the night. Mother got out the guidebook and unfolded the map. "Just a little farther, and only a short distance off the highway, there's a big lake called Lake Ilopango. It's supposed to be quite a resort area, so there should be some place where we can camp. And," she added, "we can call this our sightseeing for El Salvador."

Mystery on the Rancho Grande

"Direct me to it," Father said, as he started the car. We turned off the highway and drove past some beautiful coffee plantations. Along the lake shore was a large park full of flowering trees and shrubs. The lake, the guidebook explained, was really the crater of an extinct volcano. And from the size of the lake, it must have been a tremendous explosion to have formed such a big crater.

There were mountains all around it except for the park where we were. Just as we arrived, the sun was sinking behind the mountains in a gorgeous sunset. An attendant in the park explained to us where we could camp. He also pointed to a list of rules printed on a signboard. For instance, you weren't allowed to use soap in the lake; there were showers for regular bathing.

We all went in swimming right away. And in the morning before we left I took another dip while Mother fixed breakfast. It was really so lovely there, I hated to leave.

El Salvador is the smallest country in Central America, and we arrived at the border by mid-morning. After the usual delay at customs, we drove on into Honduras.

The road through Honduras runs quite near the Pacific, and we could see the blue water off to the west. Along the highway we saw lots of tiny houses that

Where the Pigs Wear Shoes

Mother called *chozas*. They were made of bamboo poles, with dirt floors and thatched roofs. Some of them didn't even have any windows. We had already seen quite a lot of these *chozas*, not just in Honduras, but in southern Mexico and Guatemala and El Salvador, too. It made me wonder what kind of a house we'd have on the ranch. I hoped it would be a little better than most of the ones we had seen along the highway.

Then the road twisted upward again, into some dry, rocky, desolate hills. We hardly saw anybody. Once in a great while there was a small house—usually built of stone because there wasn't much else to build with. We didn't even see many freight trucks, which had been numerous almost everywhere else. It was a lonely stretch of road, and it was beginning to get dark.

"What's the next town?" Daddy asked.

Mother studied the map. "It doesn't look as if there are any more towns until we get almost to the border of Nicaragua."

Daddy doesn't like to drive after dark, but he decided it would be better to keep going until we reached a less lonely place to camp for the night. We hadn't gone much farther when, rounding a hairpin curve, we nearly ran into a drove of pigs waddling slowly along in the middle of the highway. Dad swerved sharply to avoid them, and the truck hit a deep pothole at the side of

49

the road with an awful bump. Here we stopped to let them pass.

The pigs were being driven by a man who carried a long stick which curved at one end like the crooks that shepherds carry in old Mother Goose books. But what astonished us most was that all the pigs were wearing little leather shoes.

"Who ever saw pigs wearing shoes!" I exclaimed.

Where the Pigs Wear Shoes

"The man must be driving them quite a distance," Dad said, "so he's put shoes on them to keep their feet from getting sore."

We watched until the pigs slowly disappeared around the curve. Then Dad started the car. But we only went as far as the next little bump, when the car began to make the most terrible noise.

"Broken spring!" Dad declared, frowning.

As soon as he found a level place, he pulled off the road. "I guess we'll have to camp here," he said. "We'll worry about fixing the car in the morning. It's too dark now."

Mother made us some sandwiches and stirred up some malted milk—with powdered milk, of course. Then we got ready for bed. Daddy put his machete where he could get at it easily. "Among its other uses, the machete is an excellent defense weapon," he joked.

Well, nothing happened during the night—no bandits came out of the hills or anything—and we all slept soundly.

In the morning while Daddy was examining the damage to the car, Mother studied the map. "What are we going to do?" she asked. "It looks as though we're at least two hundred miles from the next town of any size. And you can't repair a car spring here— there's nothing to repair it with."

Mystery on the Rancho Grande

Dad was grinning as he emerged from under the car. "You forget, I have a machete—the Latin-American wonder tool."

"This is no time for teasing," Mother answered almost crossly.

"I'm not teasing," Dad said. "You wait, and stop worrying."

He climbed down a steep, rocky hillside to where some small saplings were growing. With his machete he cut one of them.

I really don't understand too much about cars, but it was wonderful to watch him whittle down the little tree trunk and make it the shape of a spring. Then he lashed it into place with some wire. As I said before, my Dad can fix just about anything.

"If we go slowly, this should hold us until we get to a service station," he said.

Within an hour we were on our way again, and by ten o'clock we were over the border into Nicaragua. There didn't seem to be many people living in this northern part of the country, but finally we came to a pretty good-sized town called Estelí. Here we found a service station that fixed the car, and very quickly. Then we were on our way again.

Farther on, the road followed the shore of Lake Managua. Then it ran between Lake Managua and

Where the Pigs Wear Shoes

Lake Nicaragua, curving around to Managua, the capital of Nicaragua.

Managua is quite a big city, but it's hot there because it's low. Many of the people have their homes in the hills that lie to the south of the city. And what a view they have of the city and the lake!

After that, the road ran by the west side of Lake Nicaragua, which is the largest lake south of the Great Lakes. There's really just a narrow strip of land between Lake Nicaragua and the Pacific, and in places we could see the lake and the ocean at the same time.

I kept hoping that the road would go closer to the Pacific. This was the third time I had seen it from a distance. But the highway kept close to the lake. I was sure that if I asked Dad to turn off and go down to the ocean he'd just say, "Aren't you seeing enough water, with a lake right beside us so big you can't see across it?" So I kept quiet.

Finally, we came to a town where we stopped for gas. When Daddy got out of the car, he took the map with him. After the tank was filled, he went into the station and I could see him talking to the attendant.

It was just like Daddy not to say anything until we'd driven on for quite a distance. Then he suddenly turned off the highway toward the ocean, saying, "The fellow at the gas station told me it's only four or five miles out to the ocean by this road. There's a port there, and a good beach. It's a little late to drive to the border tonight, and all the land along the lake seems to be privately owned. So I thought we might as well go out to this place. What's the name of it, Lisa?"

"San Juan del Sur," Mother read from the map.

I was so tickled that I hardly knew what to say. The road was paved, so we were there in no time. The town was on a little bay shaped like a half-moon.

"The whole bay doesn't look more than a mile wide," Dad said when we saw it.

At one side there were wharves where ocean ships docked. In the center of the curve were a couple of small hotels, a dance hall, and a few private homes and cottages. And there was lots of room to park beside the road that ran along the edge of the wide, sandy beach.

Well, we weren't exactly slow getting into the water. There were hardly any waves, just gentle swells that made a lovely rippling sound when they reached the sandy beach. I could see why Balboa named it the Pacific Ocean.

We all swam and swam, and afterwards made supper on our camp stove. When I went to bed that night I was tingling with happiness. I had finally had a swim in the Pacific.

And tomorrow we'd be in Costa Rica.

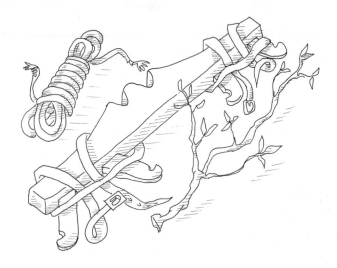

5. The Green Land

We had hardly driven a half-mile beyond the Costa Rican border when Daddy said, "See, everything looks different here. Even the grass is taller. Greener, too."

I knew he was teasing Mother so I added, "And isn't the sky a deeper blue?"

"Much deeper," he said.

"Go ahead and tease me," Mother said good-naturedly. "But before we've gone very far you'll see that it *is* different. Costa Rica is the most democratic country in the world. Do you know that—"

"—Costa Rica has more school teachers than soldiers." Dad and I finished her sentence together; we knew what she was going to say because we'd heard it so many times.

Mother laughed. "I am very happy if that fact has really penetrated."

It was our turn to laugh.

"There's something else I hope this trip has taught you both," she added, "and that is that each Latin-American country differs from the others. Each has its own personality. In Guatemala, for instance, a majority of the people are Indians and many still wear their traditional costumes. But in El Salvador and Nicaragua and Costa Rica there are few pure Indians, and the people dress as we do in the United States. In Costa Rica, most of the farmers own their own land. But in some other countries, nearly all the land is owned by a few people and everyone else works for them."

We were whizzing along now over a smoothly paved road. Instead of the thatched *chozas* we had seen so often all through Central America, nearly all the houses were built of wood and looked very well kept. None of them had screens, though. Mamma said this was because in most parts of Costa Rica, especially the highlands, there were very few flies or mosquitoes. That was another thing that surprised me about the tropics. I had always supposed that the farther south you went, the more bugs there would be.

The Green Land

Most of the houses were brightly painted. Pink and sky blue appeared to be the favorite colors, with yellow and green the next choices. Sometimes the front of a house would be pink, the porch blue and the sides yellow, trimmed with green.

"Some paint salesman must have made a fortune here," Dad commented.

"Laugh if you want to," Mother said, "but paint is a sign of prosperity in many places around the world, and to me, bright colors denote optimism."

The paint on the houses, though, was nothing compared to the paint on the oxcarts we passed. Not only the carts, but the yokes on the oxen's heads were covered with all sorts of fancy designs.

Another thing I noticed was the unusual way the oxen were yoked. Mother explained that in Costa Rica the yokes are put on the oxen's heads instead of on their necks and fastened with straps around their horns. This way, the oxen can pull with their weight thrown against their strong, broad foreheads.

For a couple of hours we drove through flat cattle-raising country. Then we got into hills again and began gradually to ascend onto the *Meseta Central*, or the central highlands, that Mother so often talked about. Here the towns were larger and closer together, and there were miles of coffee *fincas*. That's Spanish for "farms."

57

Mystery on the Rancho Grande

It was mid-afternoon when we finally reached San José, and the traffic was quite heavy. I was surprised at what a big, bustling city it is, with quaint streets and little shops, and every now and then a building as modern as anything in Dallas.

"About one-third of the population of Costa Rica is concentrated in and around San José," Mother said. "Nearly three-quarters of the people live on this high *Meseta,* while the rest of the country is quite sparsely settled."

Now Mother began giving Dad directions about how to get to her family's house. And of course there was the usual confusion: "Turn left at the next corner." "I can't; it's a one-way street." "Can't you go around the block?" You know the sort of thing.

Finally we came to a side street where all the houses were rather old and came right out to the sidewalk. Then Mother pointed to one house and said, "That's it. Stop here, while I go to the door."

A moment later she was ringing the bell, and my grandfather and grandmother Marquez came out the door, and there was a lot of hugging and kissing. Of course they'd never seen Daddy or me before, so it took quite a while.

Then Grandpa opened a big double door, and Dad drove our car into a garage that was big enough for the trailer too. Grandpa was quite tall, though thin, and he had gray hair. Grandma was just the opposite—short and plump, with a round, smiling face. Her hair and her eyes were black.

Mother had often told me you can't tell anything about a Latin-type house from its outside, but even so, I really got a surprise when I went inside. It was the most beautiful place! They just didn't waste any space on a front yard, which gave the house a nondescript look from the street. There were many rooms, and all along one side ran a kind of porch they call a gallery with a row of columns holding up the roof. It had the most elegant tile floor I had ever seen. The rest of the space was taken up by a patio with a high wall around it. This was paved with tiles, too, except for a dozen or more flower beds. In these, there were roses and calla lilies and begonias and lots of flowering shrubs, and there were vines growing up the walls. And all along the edge of the roof over the gallery were orchids hung in pots.

There was plenty of room for us, since all of Mother's brothers and sisters were married and lived in their own houses. I loved both of my grandparents right away. Having a grandchild with red hair, though, seemed to really astonish them. The only pictures they'd ever seen of me had been in black and white.

Grandma got busy and telephoned all our relatives, and before the evening was over, I was up to my ears in aunts and uncles and cousins. After all the years I'd been hearing about them, it was wonderful to finally meet them face to face. On my father's side, in the States, I had very few relatives, but here I had dozens of them.

I especially liked my cousin Cristina Ortez, who was my age, and her ten-year-old sister, Eva. Most of the other cousins were either a lot older or a lot younger.

Mystery on the Rancho Grande

All the children were out of school because this was their summer vacation. Their school year starts in March and runs until the end of November. At school in Texas I had learned that in countries south of the equator the seasons are opposite from ours—while we're having summer, they're having winter and vice versa. But now I learned that in many Latin countries that are north of the equator they call December, January, February and March "summer" because these months are drier. Warmer, too, because there are fewer clouds in the sky then and the sun shines more brightly.

We were going to stay for two or three days in San José because Daddy had to go to the customs office and pay duty on the things we had brought with us. He also had to see about getting a special permit to stay in the country and work. Luckily, Uncle Pablo worked in a government office and offered to help Daddy with all this red tape.

The next morning, Mother and her sister (my Aunt Isabel) and Cristina and Eva and I went sight-seeing. First we went to a zoo in a lovely little park. It had only animals and birds found in Costa Rica. "But these aren't all the kinds of animals we have," Aunt Isabel said.

There were jaguars and tapirs and wild pigs and monkeys and lots of smaller animals I'd never heard of

The Green Land

before. We saw a rodent, as big as a good-sized dog, called a *tepeizcuintle*. Another was an animal shaped somewhat like a sable, only black, and much bigger, that was called a *tolomuco*. The one I liked best, though, was a spotted feline about half again as big as a house cat that was called a *manigordo*. Its fur looked so soft that I wished I could pet it. Aunt Isabel said people sometimes do make pets of them, although both their teeth and their claws are awfully sharp.

From the zoo we walked to the National Museum, which is inside an ancient fortress that was built by the first settlers to protect themselves against pirates or Indians. Mother hadn't been there before because it wasn't there when she left Costa Rica—the museum, I mean; the fortress was built over three hundred years ago. It has walls three or four feet thick, and it stands on a hill overlooking the whole city. Inside were all sorts of Indian relics, including some marvelous gold and silver jewelry the Indians used to make.

On the way back to the house I saw the school where Mother went when she was a girl. She taught there later, and Eva and Cristina were going there now.

"If you'd like to have Tamara stay with us and go to school with Cristina," Aunt Isabel told Mamma, "we'd love to have her."

"Maybe in another year," Mother said, "after she's

finished seventh grade and her Spanish has improved."

We walked all the way, most of the time through parks—there are so many of them in San José. All the while Cristina and Eva kept asking me questions about the United States.

"Weren't you afraid, living where the people all carry revolvers and are always shooting at each other?" Eva asked.

At first I couldn't think what she meant. Then I realized she thought Texas was still the way they show it in Western movies. Evidently the kids back in Dallas aren't the only ones who have funny notions about other countries.

Dinner was ready when we got home. The Costa Ricans have dinner at noon, and afterwards everyone takes a *siesta* (nap) for an hour or so. I found I might as well, too, because there's not much else you can do. Everything closes down for about two hours—stores and offices and even the schools.

After *siesta*, Grandma served coffee to the grownups and had the maid make a fruit-juice drink for me. They called it a *refresco*. It was made of a fruit called *tamarindos*. While we sat on the gallery sipping our drinks, Grandpa started telling me about when he was a boy in Spain. He had gone to a university in Madrid, and had become a teacher.

The Green Land

"Did you come from Spain, too?" I asked Grandma.
"I was born here," she said, "but my ancestors came from Spain. Most Costa Ricans can trace their ancestry back to Spain. Some of my people were among the very first settlers who came here over four hundred years ago."

They told me then about how, back in the sixteenth century, Spain had sent out a few hundred settlers to Costa Rica. But there wasn't much gold or silver here, so the officials in charge of the expedition went off to Peru and Mexico where they found much more. They practically forgot about the people they had left in Costa Rica and very few new people came.

The settlers had had a hard time at first. They had to fight the Indians, just like the first settlers in the United States. They huddled together for protection on the *Meseta Central* and gradually pushed the Indians off it. The climate was wonderful—about seventy degrees most of the time—and the ground was rich, and somehow they survived and prospered in their new home. Even so, Costa Rica still has a small population for its size.

The next day Mother and I went walking by ourselves and we saw downtown San José. In this part of town there aren't any trees, most of the streets are quite narrow, and there are hardly any tall buildings. There are no really big department stores either, but lots of small shops.

On our way, we stopped in to see the National Theater, which is right downtown and is open all day so that tourists can go through it. "This has been called the most beautiful building in the Western Hemisphere," Mother said.

It really was beautiful. I had never seen so many kinds and colors of marble. It has statues everywhere and gold trimmings and lots of paintings on the walls. On the ceilings, too.

That night at supper, Daddy started talking about when we should leave for the ranch. It was already Thursday, and he had to start work the following Monday. He said that we would need a weekend to get unpacked, and suggested that we leave the next morning. All our relatives wanted us to stay a little longer, but they could understand his wanting some time to get settled on the ranch.

Then Grandma said, "Maybe Lisa and Tamara could stay here while you get settled, and then you could come back for them."

Daddy shook his head. "It would be too far, I'm afraid. And I don't know when I could get enough time off to make the trip. Besides, that drive over the mountains . . . ."

The Green Land

Grandma looked puzzled. "Just where is this ranch?" she asked.

There was the oddest silence in the room; you could have heard a pin drop. It seems that no one had told Grandma that we were going to live in the General Valley, on the other side of the Talamancas. Evidently Mother had left that detail out of her letters when she wrote that we were coming to Costa Rica. Now there was no keeping it from her any longer.

You'd have thought from the way she reacted that we were going to live in an igloo on a polar ice cap. She was just old-fashioned enough to feel that nice people never live anywhere but on the *Meseta*. It took both Uncle Pablo and Uncle Diego to convince her that nowadays things had changed and that lots of nice people were moving down into this rich valley, which until recently had been almost unpopulated. And going over the Talamancas was no longer so difficult since the Inter-American highway had been extended. Soon the road would even be paved.

I think she was only half convinced that we would be safe way off in the General Valley, but she promised to try not to worry about us. And we promised that we'd come back for a visit as soon as we could.

6. Frontier—Costa Rican Style

Next morning, after a long siege of good-byes and come-again-soons, we got away. Before we left, though, Dad put his directions for locating Mr. Ainsley's ranch where he could easily get at them. And Mother pulled sweaters out of suitcases for all of us. "We'll need them going over the mountains," she said.

Finding our way out of San José was a job. But finally, after about a dozen wrong turns, we got back on the Inter-American highway headed toward Panama.

The next large town we came to was Cartago. "It used to be the capital of Costa Rica," Mother said. "But in 1910 there was a terrible earthquake that nearly destroyed the city. After that, the capital was moved to San José."

"Look," she pointed to the ruins of a cathedral that must have been enormous. Now only parts of its great stone walls were left, and I tried to imagine what it must have been like during an earthquake strong enough to shake down a church of that size.

Just after we left Cartago, our paved road—paved all the way from Texas—came to an end. After that, it was dirt and gravel. And bumps. Dad had to drive slowly. Even so, we thought that our poor car would shake to pieces.

I thought we had seen some mountains in Mexico and Guatemala. But going over the Talamancas on an unpaved road made all those other mountains seem like little hills by comparison. After we'd gone around what must have been our thousandth hairpin curve, we found ourselves suddenly looking down on Cartago! There it lay, cuddled in its lovely, green, mountain-rimmed valley. We'd been driving for nearly an hour but we hadn't come far at all—we'd just been winding slowly upwards.

Another hour passed and Mother handed out the sweaters. We needed them, too. We were getting really high now. Every once in a while we'd drive through clouds that were lying in the hollows between peaks.

Mystery on the Rancho Grande

Some were so dense that Dad would put on the car headlights. Then a few minutes later we would suddenly come out again into bright sunlight. There were very few passenger cars on the road, though we quite often passed trucks and buses.

At every turn in the road—and we never stopped turning, it seemed—there was another terrific view, each one more spectacular than the last. What cliffs and chasms and precipices and gorges! I'd often read about "breathtaking" scenery and had thought that was a silly expression. Now I had to change my mind. Some of this scenery actually made me gasp.

There were people living all along the road. The way some of their houses were perched on the mountain-sides reminded me of pictures I'd seen of Switzerland. The higher we went, the more flowers there seemed to be: flowering trees, bushes, plants, vines. A lot of the houses had those big white flowers we call Easter lilies growing around them.

Finally we came to a sign that read *"Cerro de la Muerte,"* which means "Hill of Death," and Mother asked Daddy to stop.

"We are now at 3347 meters," Mother read from the sign. "This is the highest point on the entire Inter-American highway."

"How many feet is that?" I asked.

Frontier—Costa Rican Style

"A meter is just a little over a yard," Mother answered.

"That means we're up around eleven thousand feet," Dad put in.

"Here's a little shrine where people can give thanks for having reached this point safely," said Mother.

"I feel like giving thanks that we've gotten this far with no serious accidents," Dad said, and we all crossed ourselves.

"Of course, going over the mountains in a car is easy compared with how it must have been in the old days," Mother said. "Can you imagine coming the whole distance from San José or even from Cartago on foot or on horseback? It must have taken days."

"How those early Spanish explorers managed to tramp all over this part of the world will always be a mystery to me," Dad said, looking off into the wild mountain landscape.

"When I learned about them in school, I used to imagine them sweating and nearly roasting," I said.

"Now you probably wonder how they kept warm," Mother laughed.

After that the way was mostly downhill, and before long we took off our sweaters. Going down, some of the views were even more breathtaking than going up.

Then, all of a sudden, we came to a spot from which we could see a good-sized town far below.

71

Mystery on the Rancho Grande

"That has to be San Isidro," Mother exclaimed, "lying at the very head of the General Valley, which stretches all the way to Panama."

Dad slowed down so we could have a good look. The mountains make a new-moon curve around the town, and sunlight washed it with gold. The land around it was greener than anything I'd ever seen in my life. My Irish father must have been thinking the same thing, because he said, "Ireland can't be any greener than that."

Soon we were rolling down into San Isidro. And I had never seen a place quite like it. People were bustling about, new buildings were going up, and streets were being fixed or paved. There were hardly any passenger cars, but lots of jeeps and oxcarts getting into each other's way. And people, old and young, riding in or out of town on horseback.

I saw one woman, dressed in a bright blue dress with a wide skirt that covered her knees, riding astride a fast-trotting palomino. And there was a man and a woman going down the street on two beautiful black horses, each with a child riding in front and holding a bright red umbrella. There were kids, too, sometimes two on one horse, with sacks hung behind their saddles, carrying home groceries.

There were blacksmith shops where they were busy

shoeing horses; you could look right in through their wide doors and see the sparks flying as the blacksmith hammered shoes on his anvil. And we passed lots of stores where they sold saddles and all kinds of farm and ranch supplies. It wasn't quite like the street scenes in our Western movies, and nobody carried a revolver, yet "frontier" was the only way to describe it.

"Just imagine," said Mother. "When I left Costa Rica fifteen years ago, this was just a small town, with maybe two thousand people."

"Now Ainsley says it has ten thousand," Dad said.

In the middle of town, we stopped at a market to buy supplies. We got meat and vegetables and different kinds of fruit: pineapples and plantains—they're a kind of cooking banana—and papayas, a fruit as big as a hubbard squash that's something like a muskmelon, and many more things.

They don't give you sacks to put things in—you have to bring your own. So we bought a used cloth sugar bag and filled it so full that poor Daddy had trouble carrying it back to the car.

On the way out of town, we passed a new, modern bank building, and I nudged Mother because I couldn't believe my eyes. "Look, Mamma, there's a barefoot man going into that bank!"

"Why not?" said Mother. "For all we know, he may

be the richest man in San Isidro. This is a very free country, you know. Here you don't have to wear shoes just because other people do."

I admit that gave me something to chew on as we bumped out of town.

The farther we went down into the Valley, the more beautiful it appeared. The rougher the road, too! We crossed so many rivers that I lost count of them. The water in all of them appeared cool and clear enough to drink. It came rushing over rocky beds with such a roar you could hear it above the noise of our truck engine. There were trees along all the banks because, Mother explained, there's a law in Costa Rica about leaving a certain number of feet of woods along the banks of rivers so the soil won't wash away. And, off to our left were the great, forest-covered Talamancas with their tops lost in the clouds.

"All these rivers," Mother said as we passed still another one, "flow down from the Talamancas into the General."

"And the General"—I was pronouncing it *Hen-er-al* now, the way she did—"flows into the Pacific."

We didn't pass any more towns after San Isidro, unless you could call three or four houses built near each other a town. We only now and then passed a car, though we saw plenty of people on horseback and quite

75

a few trucks hauling logs to sawmills. Some of the logs were so enormous that three made a mammoth load.

"How do we know where we are?" I finally asked Dad.

"I'm going by the number of miles we've driven since we left San Isidro," he said with an eye on his mileometer. "Should be right along here somewhere."

A few minutes later we saw a big red gate on our left. Over it was a sign with the name "Texana" painted in white letters.

As Daddy turned into the lane leading up to it, a man—tall, lean, and deeply tanned—came running out of a small wooden house nearby. He rushed up to the car and shook hands with Dad and Mother. He talked so fast I couldn't catch half of what he said. But I gathered he worked on the ranch, and he had been watching for us, as Mr. Ainsley had sent word we were on the way.

He had a horse all saddled, tied to a nearby tree. He jumped on its back and motioned us to follow him.

The road he led us over was the bumpiest yet. It angled off down into a ravine and was so rocky that I wondered how even a horse could go over it without stumbling or falling. But I was learning that the small, wiry valley horses can go just about anywhere.

We rocked and jolted until we came to quite a wide

river where Dad stopped. But the horseman didn't. He rode right into the water. When he saw we weren't following, he turned and came back toward us.

"Can we drive through the river?" Dad asked. "Our load is pretty heavy."

"Yes. The water is not high now."

"There's no bridge?" Mother asked.

"For people, yes." He pointed off to one side.

We couldn't see any bridge, but figured it was around a bend and hidden by the trees and bushes that grew thickly along the river banks.

"Let me get out and walk across," said Mother. "It will make the load that much lighter."

"Me, too," I said, scrambling out after her.

When Mother and I saw what kind of bridge it was, we might have jumped right back into the car—but by that time Daddy was already in the middle of the river with water up to his floor boards. The river was about sixty feet wide at this point, and the bridge hung about twenty feet above it. It was made of four wire cables stretched between two giant trees on opposite sides of the river. Other wires were strung between the lower two cables. And on these cross wires had been laid a row of planks about ten inches wide. You walked on the planks, hanging onto the two top wires which formed handrails.

Mystery on the Rancho Grande

Well, at first I thought I just couldn't cross it. I don't believe I ever could have if I hadn't always been a tomboy, used to climbing around. If you looked down at the water, rushing and roaring madly over the great boulders beneath, you would be dizzy in no time. The trick was to keep your eyes on the planks and not allow yourself even a little glance at the water.

I finally made it, holding my breath the whole way. Then I looked back and found that Mother wasn't coming. I tried to shout to her, "Just keep your eyes on the planks," but with the water roaring and pounding, she couldn't hear me.

In the meantime, Dad had driven the car across the ford, and when he saw the bridge, he came to help Mamma. He crossed over to where she was standing on the other side, holding on tight to the handrails. I couldn't hear what they said, but I felt very proud of her when she followed him back. I don't believe many mothers of the kids I know back in Dallas would have ever made it.

When we got back in the car, none of us spoke for quite a while. I had a hunch we were all thinking the same thing, though. Just how rugged was life on this Costa Rican ranch going to be? If this bridge was a sample . . . .

7. El Rancho Grande

We followed the horseman up out of the wooded ravine and across three separate pastures, all with herds of cattle in them. And I had a chance to see how he opened and shut all the gates between pastures without dismounting. He made it look easy. Finally, after a lot of bumping and bouncing around, we came out on a long, flat field.

"This is evidently Mr. Ainsley's airstrip," Dad said. "See the white markers along the sides."

We drove down a tree-shaded lane at one side of the airfield, and soon came to a large house. It had several smaller houses in back of it for servants or workers, and

beyond these were various barns and corrals, the hangar
for Mr. Ainsley's airplane, and other outbuildings. All
the buildings were made of wood, but only the main
house was painted. It was white, with quite a few shade
trees and some flowering shrubs around it.

The rider tied his horse—it was sweating now from
galloping to keep ahead of us—to a wire fence that surrounded the house. Then he led us through a small gate
into the yard, or "compound," as we later learned they
called it.

Before we reached the house a man came hurrying out. Dad started to introduce himself, but the man said, "Señor Perkins?" and held out his hand.

"Señor Gomez?" Dad replied. They had learned each other's names, of course, from Mr. Ainsley.

Arturo Gomez was a big, heavyset man, with small, sharp, brown eyes. His skin was swarthy and his nose rather large. Still, he wasn't bad-looking, especially as he seemed always to be half-smiling. He was wearing a wide-brimmed *sombrero* and a checkered shirt, and his trousers were tucked inside tall, black leather boots.

Right away he invited us into the big white house and introduced us to his wife, Emilia. She was a small woman with dark eyes, very straight black hair, and skin the color of brown sugar. Mother said later that she probably had some Indian blood; the Valley is one of the few places in Costa Rica where there are still some Indians left.

Señora Gomez insisted upon getting us something to eat, although we told her we'd had a snack in San Isidro. I was glad she did, though, because I was already starving again. We had steak and rice and black beans and fried *plátanos*. And for dessert we had soursop ice cream. The name didn't sound very appetizing, but it was simply delicious. I'd never heard of soursops before, so Señora Gomez showed me one out in the kitchen. It was a big, uneven-shaped, green fruit with a creamy white center dotted with jet black seeds. You strain out the seeds and use the juice to make ice cream or *refrescos*.

After we'd eaten, Señor Gomez offered to show us around. "I'll take you to our commissary first, and then we can go over to your house."

The commissary was a store in a small building between the cowbarn and the corrals. There, everybody who worked on the ranch could buy staples like flour, sugar, rice, beans, canned meats, and lots of other things.

"We run it as a convenience to our workers. It's such a long way to the nearest town," Gomez explained. "At seven in the morning a can of fresh milk is delivered from the cowbarn. You bring your own bottles or container, depending on how much you want. You get your mail here, too. And on Saturdays we have meat—usually beef, though sometimes we have pork."

"Our icebox has a good-sized freezer," Mother said. "We can lay in our week's supply every Saturday."

"That's what we do," Gomez said. "By the way," he added, turning to Mother, "you'll need a *criada*, won't you?" (A *criada* is a maid.)

"Why, yes, I was hoping to find someone to help me."

"I know a good girl I think I can get for you," he continued. "If you want me to, I'll send her over as soon as I can get in touch with her."

"That would be wonderful," said Mother.

"Now I'll show you your house."

"Can I drive over?" Dad asked.

"Yes, sure," replied Gomez.

But Mother said, "We can't all get in the car. So suppose we walk over first. Then, Wally, you can come back with Señor Gomez and bring the car."

"It's not far," Gomez said.

Mystery on the Rancho Grande

We followed a lane that led off from one side of the corrals, then alongside a big orange grove with tall trees full of ripe, golden fruit.

"You can help yourself to oranges," Gomez said. "With the market so far away, it doesn't pay to pick and haul them."

The lane led us uphill into a small field. There was a plain wooden house at the far side.

"Is that it?" I asked.

"That's it," Gomez replied.

The house was very plain and it didn't look as though it had ever been painted. But there was a big yard, enclosed by a wire fence, with quite a few trees and shrubs in it and space where you could plant a garden. There was a porch that ran halfway across the front, a living room, two bedrooms, a bath, and a kitchen, with another room in back of the kitchen for a maid. One of the bedrooms was right in front, at one end of the porch. Mother said I could have that one, if I wanted it.

The house was furnished with beds and dressers and tables and chairs, but I was surprised to see that the walls and ceilings weren't plastered. There were just wide boards, with all the beams showing, like in summer cottages I had seen in the States. There weren't any panes of glass in the windows, either—only heavy

wooden shutters you could close if it rained very hard.

In a way it was a nice house, but I had been hoping it would be more like the house we'd had in Texas. I didn't want to upset Mother by telling her how I felt about it, so after Dad went back with Gomez to get the car, I walked around outside for a while.

Mystery on the Rancho Grande

I discovered that there was a deep ravine nearby, with a creek running through it, and with woods along both banks. It was so beautiful that I stopped thinking about the house not being painted or plastered the way I had hoped. Even when I got back up on the porch, I could still hear the little river splashing and gurgling over its stony bed. From a distance it sounded like lovely soft music.

When I went back inside Mother said, "The house isn't much, but I think I can make it quite attractive. Maybe later we can paint it, and perhaps we can plant some flowers around it."

A few moments later Daddy drove up. He had two peons with him that Señor Gomez had sent along to help us unload. I found out that in the Valley it's all right to call a worker a peon. In Texas if you called a man a peon he'd be insulted. But down here the workers who aren't cowboys or carpenters or something like that, call themselves peons.

By the time the men had lugged all our stuff up on the porch (Mother didn't want it inside until she could clean the place), the girl came over. Her name was Flor. She was about twenty, I guessed, rather small and brown like Señora Gomez, with straight black hair. But she was very strong and a wonderfully quick worker. In no time she had the house all scrubbed.

86

El Rancho Grande

Later we were all in the kitchen together. I was un-packing dishes, Flor was washing out the cupboards, Daddy was connecting up the washing machine, and Mother was sorting over clothes that had to be washed.

Then Mother asked, "Do you speak English, Flor?"

Evidently Flor caught her name for she turned toward Mother, but with a completely blank stare.

"You don't know any English at all? You don't speak English?" Mother repeated. Then she said, *"No habla ingles?"*

The girl shook her head.

"If she doesn't understand that," Daddy said, "she can't understand anything. 'Speak English,' like *'habla español,'* is just about the first thing anyone learns."

"That's fine—just what I hoped." Mother shot a glance at me. "If she can't speak a word of English, Tamara's going to *have* to speak to her in Spanish."

"Your score," I grinned.

About four in the afternoon Señora Gomez came over. She invited us to have supper with them that evening.

"We have some groceries—" Mother started to protest.

But Señora Gomez insisted. "You must be tired. Never mind cooking tonight. Come and eat with us."

We did, and had some delicious chicken and rice. This time for dessert we had a custard pudding the Latins call *flan.*

Mystery on the Rancho Grande

By the time we finished supper it was completely dark. That was something else I learned about the tropics—how short the twilight is.

"Right on the equator," Mother said, "there's almost no twilight. One minute it's light and the next it's dark. Here, at least, we have a short time between day and night."

Señor Gomez got a flashlight and walked with us to our *casita,* as they call a small house.

Nobody could have been nicer or kinder to us than Señor and Señora Gomez. I liked her, but I felt positively ashamed that I couldn't make myself like him even a little. Evidently Mother felt the same way I did. After we got back to our house, she and Dad sat in the living room talking. I was so tired that I went to bed right away, but I could hear their conversation from my room.

"Gomez seems like a genial sort of person," Dad said. "Should be easy to work with. What did you think of him?"

Mother didn't answer right away. Then she said slowly, "I—well, perhaps I shouldn't say anything until I know more about him, but I got a funny feeling that he was being *too* nice."

"What do you mean?" asked Dad. "You're the one who's always saying that Costa Ricans are friendly people. He was probably just trying to make us feel at home."

"That's not what I meant," Mother said.

"Then what do you mean?" Dad asked.

"Didn't you notice this afternoon how the peons seemed to cringe every time he spoke to them? They didn't appear to think he was such a genial fellow. In fact, I wouldn't be surprised if they were really afraid of him."

Then Dad said, "I must admit I never shook hands with a man who gave me such a clammy feeling. His hand felt exactly like a cold, dead fish."

"Anyhow, I think you'd be wise to watch your step with him until you know him better," said Mother. "Maybe I'm imagining the whole thing, but it won't hurt to be cautious in the beginning. It's always harder to judge people of another nationality, and a lot depends on how you get along with him."

"I guess you're right," Dad said. "I'll watch my step until I get the feeling of the place. But Ainsley thinks Gomez is a good man, so I'm sure everything will work out."

"I certainly hope so," Mother said. "I'm glad to be home."

"So am I," said Dad.

8. Beyond the Seven Falls

The next thing I knew, something suddenly woke me
up. It was morning, just getting light, and a frightful
racket filled the air. It sounded as though a freight train
filled with rusty jingle bells was flying overhead.

I ran out into the living room and yelled to Mother
and Dad, "What is it?"

Mother put her head out of their bedroom door—she
was brushing her hair—and said, "Oh, that's a flock of
parakeets. They must have been roosting last night in
a tree near here. When they fly off in the morning, they
all start screaming at once."

I looked out of the window just in time to see the

flock circling around over the house. They were a much larger kind of parakeet than the ones you see in cages in the States. They were a beautiful green, and they flew very high and fast. They seemed to be all scream-ing at each other: "Wait for me . . . Where are we going? . . . What's the rush? . . . Come on, birds, get going . . ." and so on, like a bunch of kids taking off on a picnic.

I returned to my room to get dressed. I'd hardly finished and gone back to the living room again when I heard a bell ding-dong.

Mother was helping Flor set the table for breakfast. "That must be the work bell," she said.

"Work bell!" I cried. "People don't start work this early, do they?"

"They certainly do—in Costa Rica. This is probably the world's earliest-rising country."

"But why? What's the hurry?" I inquired.

"You'll find out."

"Is it a secret?"

Mother sat down at the table and began pouring us all orange juice from a big pitcher. "We're in the dry season now," she explained. "But during the year it rains a great deal here—four or five times as much as it does in the part of Texas where we lived. That's what keeps the country so green, of course. But nearly all the rain falls after two or three in the afternoon, or at night. In the morning the sun usually shines, so people have learned to get their work or errands done in the mornings while the weather is fine. In San José the schools all begin at seven and most of the stores are open at least by eight."

"Seven!" I pulled a chair up to the table and dropped into it.

"You'll get used to it. Not only that, but you'll like it. The mornings here are too beautiful to waste in bed."

After breakfast Mother and I walked over to the commissary, taking along a covered pot to get milk in. We were just in time to see some of the *vaqueros* (cowboys) riding out of the corrals to go to work. The way they rode you'd think they were glued to their saddles. A few minutes later two men brought a big can of milk over from the cowbarn. Then a lot of the wives and children of the *vaqueros* and peons began coming for milk. Some of them were blond, but quite a few looked more Indian than Spanish, though nearly all were quite tanned.

I found out later that the ranch was quite near an Indian reservation. They don't have reservations like those in the United States, but the Costa Rican government passed a law forbidding the Indians to sell, or anyone to buy land in certain areas. This way, they

would always have a place to live. Some of the Indians from the reservation had gotten jobs on the *finca*.

I was hoping that there would be some girls of my age. But I only saw one, and guess what! She was toting a baby in one arm and her dish for milk in the other.

"Your baby?" Mother asked her.

She nodded.

"How old are you?"

"Thirteen," she answered.

Well, that certainly gave me something to think about. If all the girls my age were already married, who was I going to pal around with?

When Mother and I got back to the house we found Flor had been working up a storm. She had the dishes done, the beds made, and was just putting a load of clothes in the washing machine.

"It's really amazing," Mother said. "You usually have to train these girls to do every little thing. Most of them don't even know how to make a bed. But this girl seems to know just how to go at everything."

"Aren't you glad?" I asked. I was, because it meant that I wouldn't have to help so much around the house.

"Of course I am. I'm just surprised, that's all, to find a girl down here who is so efficient."

Meanwhile Daddy had unhitched the car from the trailer and had gone off on a little expedition of his own. When he came back, he had nails and some boards he'd gotten from the ranch repair shop. He didn't have to start on his regular job until Monday, so he set to work putting up shelves and making more places for us to hang things.

I could hardly wait to explore the ranch, but the grass was still drenched with dew, and I decided I'd better wait a while before starting out. Besides, I knew that I should help some more with our unpacking. But after about an hour, I asked Mother if it would be all right if I went for a little walk.

"If you follow the lanes and paths and don't go too far," she said.

"I won't go far," I promised.

I started following a trail that went toward the mountains. It was so narrow and rocky that even a jeep probably couldn't have driven along it. I guessed it was for oxcarts, maybe. And horses.

I crossed a couple of fields, being careful to shut each gate after I went through it. Even though we hadn't lived on a ranch since I was nine, I still remembered how important it is to always shut gates on a farm or ranch where there are animals that could stray.

After a while I came to another gate, but this time it was the kind that Dad always called an "Okie" gate back in Texas. It was made of strands of barbed wire fastened to three or four sticks or poles. At the ends were two stout posts with wire loops at the top and bottom. To open or shut the gate you have to slide the top loop off the end pole of the gate. The bottom one then comes loose easily.

Usually these gates are easy enough to open; the trick is to shut them afterwards. Everything depends on how tight the wires have been pulled, and you can't always tell about that by looking at them. And, knowing how

important it is on a ranch never to leave a gate open, I decided not to take a chance, and slid under the fence instead.

Soon I came to the most beautiful stream I'd seen yet. It wasn't wide, not over thirty or forty feet, and the trail led right through it at a spot where it was shallow and easy to ford. Nearby a long tree trunk had been laid across the river as a foot bridge. Above it and a little to one side, a heavy wire had been strung to serve as a handrail.

I walked out to the middle of the bridge, hanging onto the wire to steady myself. There I stopped to have a look at the river. As I said before, I could never walk over a narrow bridge like that and look at the water at the same time; that would make me dizzy as anything. But standing still, I could look all I wanted to.

And what a sight! From the middle of the "bridge," I could see seven different waterfalls—five above and two below me—where the water tumbled and rumbled and swished and roared over great boulders.

I would have loved to follow the stream, but the woods along it were so dense that it would have been almost impossible. Besides the trees, there were all sorts of vines and bushes and lots of those big lianas—you know, the bushropes Tarzan is always swinging on.

After a while I decided to climb out of the ravine on

the opposite side of the river to see what was beyond the woods. Where the trees ended I came to another fence and another Okie gate. I slid under this one, too, and kept on walking.

The pasture beyond was big and hilly with very tall grass—over my head in most places. I couldn't see very far ahead, but I decided that there probably weren't any cattle in the field because the grass was so high. In every cow pasture I'd ever seen, the grass was eaten off close to the ground.

I followed the path across the field a little farther, and then a little farther still. But I hadn't gone a great distance when someone on horseback came riding down the trail toward me. I stepped to one side into the grass to let him pass. It was a nice-looking boy of about fourteen, tall, quite tanned, and with brown hair and eyes. I don't know what startled him—whether it was because he hadn't seen me walking toward him, or if he was unprepared to see a girl alone in the field, or if it was my red hair (which is rare in Costa Rica, especially in the Valley). Anyway, whatever it was, he looked so surprised that it was a wonder he didn't fall off his horse.

"*Buenos días,*" I said, because I'd already learned it was the custom to speak to everyone you met on the ranch.

Beyond the Seven Falls

He answered with *"Adiós,"* which Costa Ricans use both for "hello" and "good-bye."

I walked a little farther, and when I came to a high place, I turned around to watch him ride through the river. It really amazed me to see the way his horse dashed right through the water without slowing down, as if it were the same as dry land. All of a sudden, then, the boy turned around and caught me looking at him. I waved and he waved and then we both went on.

I still didn't see any sign of cattle in the field, so I kept going just a little farther. Finally, I saw another woods ahead; a real forest, it seemed—not just strips along the banks of a river. And there was another Okie gate, but again I went under the fence instead of trying to open and shut it.

The trail into the woods was gorgeous. The trees were tall and thick, nearly blotting out the sun. But the tangle of vines and bushes growing among the tree trunks and the orchids and airplants hanging onto everything made it seem dreadfully spooky.

Ahead of me I could hear the rush of another river and I wanted to go far enough to see it. But all of a sudden I began to hear noises—like small twigs being broken. I thought some animal must be stalking me and breaking twigs as it moved through the dense underbrush.

Mystery on the Rancho Grande

My heart gave a kind of lurch and for a moment I thought it was stuck in my throat. I turned around and looked carefully into the woods. I didn't see anything, but I hurried back to the open field. I had to lean on the fence there for a little while to catch my breath. I think I hadn't realized how scared I was until then. Now I had time to remember what Mother had said about the larger forests in the Valley having wild animals in them.

After a minute I started back through the big pasture with the tall grass. The walking was easier because the trail was more downhill now, since I was going away from the mountains.

I was feeling a little calmer as I walked toward the top of a small hill. But when I reached the top, I saw an immense herd of cattle ahead of me. There must have been at least three hundred of them, and they were stretched out right across my trail. They'd probably been in the field all the time, only down in some hollow where I couldn't see them.

How, I wondered, was I going to get past them? I was afraid to go off the trail because the grass was too thick to walk through. I couldn't see a tree nearby to climb, and I was afraid to go back to the forest, remembering all those queer crackling sounds.

For a moment I stood there, trying to decide what to

do. I knew from having lived on a ranch that it's wrong to run from cattle. That only makes them chase you. Better to face them—but with a stick in hand. The only trouble was that I didn't have a stick and I couldn't see one anywhere. But I finally picked up a couple of stones.

I was hoping maybe the herd would just pass on by without seeing me and go down into some other ravine. I even thought of crawling deep into the grass to hide. But if I did that, I wouldn't be able to see the cattle at all and I might suddenly find myself right in the middle of them.

Then, all of a sudden, one of them—probably a leader, since all herds have leaders that the rest follow —saw me. Right away it started to come toward me, with all the others following. I knew then that it was too late to run. I could never reach the woods before the herd did. Cattle can run awfully fast when they want to. I was still looking for a stick, but there weren't any nearby. Meanwhile, the herd had come. close enough so that I saw they weren't cows, but young steers—big Brahman cattle, every one of them weighing eight or ten times as much as I did.

Although I knew it was the wrong thing to do, I started walking very fast back toward the forest. When I looked over my shoulder, they were rapidly gaining on me! I started to run—and they all began running, too, or at least hurrying. Finally I turned around and shouted at them, "Whey! Whey!" and threw my stones. They stopped for a minute, but then they started toward me again.

My heart was up in my throat and I could hardly breathe. I was so scared I felt almost paralyzed. My legs didn't seem to belong to me any more. I was sure I'd never make it to the woods before they caught up with me.

Just then I saw a huge boulder off to one side of the trail. I fought my way through the grass toward it. It wasn't easy climbing, but I scrambled up somehow, gripping with the flat of my hands and finding small footholds with my sneakers.

I was trembling so much by the time I got up on top of it that I was almost afraid to stand up, lest I lose my balance and fall off again. Finally I managed to steady myself enough to stand up straight.

By that time the herd was fanning out around the rock in a half-circle, with the nearest animals maybe twenty feet away. There they stopped and just stood staring at me. They stared and stared. Every now and then one would push another out of its way so it could get a better look. They acted like people in a crowd watching a street parade.

How long was I going to have to stay on that rock? I began to wonder. What if the herd came still closer? The horns of the taller steers could easily reach my legs.

Then I saw something that made me weak with joy. Two men on horseback were galloping up the trail toward me. One of them was the good-looking boy I had met when I was walking up the trail. The other was leading a third horse, saddled but riderless. I waved and they waved back. In a few minutes they had driven the cattle back and were at the foot of my rock fortress.

Our Spanish got awfully confused for a while—especially as I was too excited to talk sensibly in any language. But I found out that when Lalo, the boy, got back to the compound, he mentioned having seen a small, redheaded girl walking through the big pasture between the river and the woods. And right away Señor Gomez sent him and his father, Pedro Ibarra, after me. Pedro, who was the head *vaquero* on the ranch, happened to be up by the corrals because they were getting ready to dip some cattle to get the ticks off them.

Señor Ibarra was tall and tanned and very lean. I never saw any other man sit so straight on a horse. He was really "tall in the saddle" as they say out West.

He dismounted to help me down from the rock and

onto the horse they had brought for me. Then he shortened the stirrups so my feet would reach them. Luckily, I was wearing blue jeans.

Meanwhile he explained that the cattle probably wouldn't have hurt me. They were merely curious. They weren't used to seeing anyone on foot, much less a small *pelirroja* (redheaded girl). And they may have thought I was bringing them some salt. All the same, he didn't seem to blame me for being scared.

"Señor Gomez was afraid you might have gone into the woods," Lalo said.

"I did!" I answered.

"It's not very safe for a person as young as you are and on foot," Pedro said.

I wanted to tell them then about the twigs crackling, but decided to wait until some other time.

The ride back to the compound was really a turning point in my life. From that moment on, I was a confirmed riding fan. Up on the back of a horse I could see so much farther. And what a feeling of power and speed it gives you! If I'd been on horseback that morning, I'd have seen that herd. And I could have ridden around it, or even right through it.

This wasn't exactly the first time I'd ever been on a horse. I'd had short rides before, from the house to the barn or the corral when we lived on the ranch in West

Texas. But this was my first real ride. I was especially thrilled when we rode down the steep bank to the river, and right through the ford, and then up and out of the ravine again. And I knew then that I wanted a horse of my own more than anything else in the world.

When we arrived at the *casa grande,* as they called the big house where Señor and Señora Gomez lived, Dad and Mother were both out in the compound. Mother rushed up and kissed and hugged me. Dad hugged me, too. Then they both began scolding me at once—which was lucky in a way, because I couldn't understand what either of them was saying.

When they subsided, Señor Gomez got in his say. It had to do with the danger of poisonous snakes when you walk through tall grass in low shoes instead of boots, and the possibility of being attacked by wild animals in the great forests on the mountains. "They've been known to eat children," he said in conclusion. "You really should never go beyond the falls."

I hung my head in shame. After all, what could I say? But all the while I was thinking, "I simply must have a horse—a horse of my very own."

9. River Coasting

We had been living on the Rancho Texana for quite a few weeks before I began to have even the faintest idea of how big a ten-thousand-acre ranch really is.

In Texas or other places where the land is flatter, it wouldn't seem nearly as large. There are quite a few ranches in Texas as big or bigger (not to mention the famous King ranch which has a million acres), but there not only is the land flatter, but the ranches are usually square and cut by straight roads so you can easily drive to any part of them.

But in the *Valle de El General,* where we were, nothing is square or flat. Many of the ranch boundaries are formed by rivers or hilltop ridges, There are cliffs no horse can go up, and the trails wind around them. From what I had seen, I guessed there wasn't a straight trail on the place.

One time Dad said, "I don't suppose Ainsley himself knows exactly how many acres there are in this place. The land just reaches up into the Talamancas where I doubt if anyone has ever really surveyed."

Well, after my rescue from the rock I was forbidden to do any more exploring. I could walk the length of the airfield in one direction. Or I could walk the other way as far as the river with the seven falls. And that was about all.

"I'm beginning to feel like a prisoner," I told Dad and Mother at supper one night. "Without a horse you can't go anywhere or do anything here."

"Maybe later on we can get you a horse," Dad finally said. But he said it so uncertainly that it didn't give me much hope.

"Are they awfully expensive?" I asked.

"No. I think we could afford one. But there's the question of pasture."

"Pasture!" I exclaimed. "With all these acres and acres of grass? What difference would one more horse make?"

"Well—" Dad seemed to be stalling. "Gomez is fussy about pastures. They're for cattle; he doesn't like to put

horses in the same fields. You know, horses eat grass
down closer to the ground than cows do."

"But until I have one of my own, couldn't I ride one
of the horses here? One that isn't being used much?"

I had already learned that each of the ten *vaqueros*
on the ranch had at least three horses, because the
great distances they were ridden and the terribly rough
ground—up and down stony ridges, through rivers and
tall brush—tired them out quickly. Even though a horse
worked one day, then rested two, it was usually worn
out by the time it was about twelve years old.

"We'd have to get permission from Señor Gomez, of
course," Dad answered. Again he had a dragging-his-
feet sound.

"Couldn't you ask him?" I coaxed.

"I'd rather not just now. Not until I have a better
idea how things are going."

That was the first inkling I had that things might
not be going so well for Dad. He hadn't let on at all. But
suddenly I realized something was bothering him.

"Aren't things going well?" I asked.

Mother didn't wait for Dad to answer. She said,
rather sharply, "Let your father eat his supper."

I dropped the subject then, of course. But a few days
later I asked Dad, "Will you let *me* ask Señor Gomez if
I can have a horse to ride sometimes?"

I could see Dad wasn't too pleased with the idea, but he finally said, "All right. Go ahead."

A couple of days later, Mother sent me over to the commissary for some rice. Señor Gomez was there, going over some accounts. He greeted me and smiled as always, so I thought this would be a good time to bring up the subject.

"Señor Gomez," I began, "I need to learn to ride if I live down here. Dad says maybe later he might buy me a horse. But until then I wonder if I couldn't borrow one once in a while."

"Why, certainly, you need to learn to ride." He seemed to agree with me perfectly. "Unfortunately, right now we don't have a horse that I'd consider safe enough for you to mount. Most of our horses are pretty wild, you know. I wouldn't want you to get hurt."

"If you do have one—maybe later—?"

"Of course. You can count on it," he said.

Well, after that I could hardly get home fast enough to tell Mother and Dad. It was late afternoon, and Dad was already home from work.

When I told them what Señor Gomez had said, Mother exclaimed, "Why, that's wonderful."

But Dad only went "Hmph!" in a funny way that wasn't like him at all.

"What do you mean 'Hmph'?" I asked.

110

River Coasting

"I just mean that Señor Gomez has some of the smoothest ways of saying 'no' of any human being I ever met."

My spirits took a nose dive. "You mean you don't believe he really intends—?"

"We'll see." Dad was so curt I decided I better drop the subject for a while.

But after that, every time I saw Señor Gomez I would ask, "Any horse yet I can ride?"

"Not yet. But one of these days."

"You won't forget?"

"You can count on me." He'd say it so cheerily that you'd really think he was sincere. Yet, little by little, I began to see what Dad meant. Gomez always said "yes," but he might as well have said "no" for all the good it did me. So the days went by and I still had no horse.

Maybe it was to get my mind off horses that Dad asked Pedro Ibarra where there was a good place to swim. Although there were many rivers in the Valley, most of them were too swift and too shallow for swimming.

Pedro said that on Sunday his son Lalo would take us to a good place. We didn't go to church very often because there wasn't any church yet in that part of the Valley. Once a month a *padre* from San Isidro would hold mass in a schoolhouse about three miles away. He

was quite young and rode around on a motorcycle—
that is, where there were roads. Where there were no
roads he went on horseback.

About ten o'clock on Sunday morning Lalo rode up.
Since we didn't have horses, he left his tied to our fence
and we walked from there. Dad and I had to coax
Mother to come with us. At first she thought she
couldn't leave. But then we reminded her that she had
a *criada*.

"I guess I'm still not used to having a maid who
can do the cooking and washing as well as the housework." She laughed at herself.

Lalo was taking us to a place on the river near the
entrance to the *finca*, not far from the scary bridge we
had crossed on the day we arrived. Only he took us by
a shortcut that I would never have found by myself,
especially since I wasn't allowed to go exploring any
more. On the way across a field I had not seen before, we
passed some long, low buildings that Lalo said were
specially built pigpens.

"I didn't know Mr. Ainsley raised pigs, too," I said.

"Yes," Lalo replied. "He has many pigs here."

We were close enough now so that I could hear the
pigs squealing and grunting.

"How many pigs does he have?" I asked.

"About sixty."

112

River Coasting

On the far side of the field we went through a gate to a lane. On the opposite side of the lane we slid under a wire fence and followed a narrow path through a woods. We could hear the river pounding and sputtering long before we saw it. In fact, wherever you went on the ranch, or for that matter in the Valley, you were hardly ever completely away from the sound of water rushing and gurgling and roaring over rocky beds.

A short distance more and we were there. It was a place where the river made a sharp turn. Opposite was a cliff that forced the water around in a curve.

It was a divine spot. Orchid-laden branches hung out over the clear, pure water, and growing up the bank of the cliff were ferns and begonias—the same kind of begonias people grow in flower gardens back home. They were in bloom now. Birds were singing in the trees, and a big, greenish kingfisher came flying around the bend.

The water was quite cool, but Lalo plunged right in. What you did was to go in just below a rocky barrier where the water starts getting deep and then let the current carry you around the bend near the cliff. After you got around, you had to swim like mad across the current to reach a stretch of beach farther down. If you didn't make it, then all you could do was to hang onto some rock until you could fight your way to shore.

113

River Coasting

It was really the craziest kind of swimming! You got a fast ride down with the current and then struggled back to shore so you could ride down again. But it was the most fun I ever had in the water.

Later, when I was sitting on a big boulder near the end of the run, catching my breath, and waiting for Lalo to ride the current down again, all of a sudden I heard that strange crackling sound in the woods behind me. Like small twigs being broken. It was a little like someone playing castanets—someone who didn't really know how to use them.

My heart jumped. I was glad when a minute later Lalo came drifting down the current toward me. After he'd pulled himself up onto a nearby boulder, I said, "Listen! Do you hear that? Like a big animal walking and stepping on little twigs!"

At first he didn't seem to know what I was talking about. But he didn't look frightened, and I could see he didn't believe there were any animals nearby.

I slipped off the boulder then and waded to the bank. "Listen!" I said when I heard the sounds again.

When I turned, Lalo was laughing. "That?" He imitated the sound with his lips.

"Yes."

"That's not an animal. They're birds," he said.

"Birds! They don't sound like birds to me."

"They're funny little birds called *manakins*," he said.

"*Little* birds! Making all that noise?"

He came over to the bank and started peering into the thick growth. "There. There's one."

I had a hard time seeing it, even though it was very brightly colored—red, yellow, orange, and black. It seemed unbelievable that such a colorful bird could hide among the leaves and flowers of the low bushes.

By this time Mother had finally gotten up courage enough to ride down the current, and she and Dad were now climbing out on the rocks where Lalo and I had been sitting. I called to them to come and see the funny little birds. But they made so much noise that by the time they got near enough to see the little flock —evidently there was a whole flock of them—the birds had moved on.

We all made our way back then to the starting place for another ride down the river. But meanwhile I had begun thinking. When Lalo and I again crawled up on the big rocks I asked him, "Are there really many wild animals in the forests here? I mean, is it really dangerous to walk through the woods alone?"

He thought a moment before he answered. "There are wild animals, it's true. But you never see the big ones like pumas and jaguars and tapirs, at least not around here. They're farther up in the mountains where the

116

forests have never been cut. Here you may see a *martilla,* or an *oso—*"

"*Oso!*" I cried. I knew that word meant "bear."

"They aren't really bears," Lalo said. "We call them that, but they're actually anteaters, or ant bears. They have long noses and very long bushy tails."

"Oh!" I exclaimed. "I didn't see any in the zoo in San José, but I've seen a picture of one on a Costa Rican stamp. It was on a letter one of my aunts wrote Mother."

"Yes, we had a stamp like that a while back."

"I'd give anything to see one. Not the stamp, but a live *oso,* I mean."

"I'll keep on the lookout. If I run into one, I'll come by and take you to see it."

"That would be wonderful!"

Then, while I was in the business of asking questions, I decided I might as well make a thorough job of it. So I said, "And snakes? Are there many snakes here? I haven't seen a single one since we came."

"There are some," he said. "Most of them aren't poisonous. We do have a few, though, that are very bad. The fer-de-lance is the worst. It has a triangular head—that's what gives it its name—and grows to be eight feet long. And then there's a very poisonous green snake. But we have so many hawks that eat snakes and are always hunting them, especially our white snake hawk, that you hardly ever see any. I guess there are a lot more in the lowlands than around here. Anyhow, it's better never to step where you can't see where you are stepping."

Then he showed me a way you could walk safely almost anywhere. You carry a stick, about four feet long, and you strike the ground or whack the bushes in front of you if you are going through tall grass or brush.

"Snakes haven't any ears," Lalo explained. "They hear vibrations with their tongues. They will usually run from you if you give them a chance."

"Isn't there a terrible snake called the bushmaster, that will chase people?" I asked.

"I've heard of them," Lalo answered, "but I don't know of anyone who ever saw one around here. Anyhow," he added, "they always keep antivenin at the commissary, just in case anyone is bitten."

We waded back, then, along the riverbank to our starting place and had another wonderful ride down and around the river bend.

While coasting with the current I did some more thinking. And after we pulled ourselves up again on the big rocks at the end of the run I asked him, "What's up past those woods where I went for a walk on my first day here—when you and your father had to rescue me?"

"More pastures," he answered. "And the *Camino Real*."

"*Camino Real*? What's that?"

"That's the ancient road the Spaniards used in the days when all Central and South America was ruled by Spain. The Spaniards traveled by that road all the way from Peru to Mexico. And up into California, too."

"I know California used to belong to Spain," I said, "and New Mexico and Arizona and Texas, too."

"Our house is on the *Camino Real*," he said. "Haven't you ever been up that way?"

"No. How could I? I don't have a horse, and they won't let me walk farther than my Seven Falls."

"Oh," Lalo said. But with such an odd expression on his face that I would have given anything to know what he was really thinking.

Just then Dad came floating down to tell us that Mother thought we had all been swimming long enough for that day. So I didn't have a chance to ask Lalo any more questions.

By that time, though, I had learned enough to have a sneaking hunch that somebody was deliberately trying to scare me and keep me from having a horse so I couldn't go exploring around the ranch.

I wondered why.

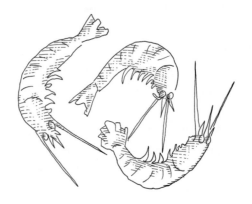

10. Lalo

We went swimming often after that. My folks wouldn't let me go alone, but I found there was one good thing about starting work so early in the morning—you got off early, too. Dad began at six, had an hour off at noon, and worked until three in the afternoon. That still left plenty of time for a swim before dark.

Lalo often went with us. I found out that his name was really Eduardo and he went to a *colegio* (high school) in San José during the school year. This was his "summer" vacation. He loved animals and wanted to become a veterinarian, so he was hoping to study at the University after he graduated from school.

120

Lalo

"Of course, if it wasn't for Mr. Ainsley giving Dad such a good job, I wouldn't be able to go to the University, or even to a *colegio*," he said. "I'd have probably just gone through the sixth grade in the country school nearest here, and that would have been the end of my education."

Lalo also told us lots of interesting things about the ranch. It was from him that we learned there was a kind of large shrimp in the rivers that was very good to eat. This was the time of year to go after them, because the water was lower than in the rainy season.

After dark is the best time to catch them, he explained. You wear rubber boots and carry a machete and a lantern or a flashlight. You look for them among the rocks along the banks of the river. And when you see a shrimp, you whack it with the back side of the machete blade.

One evening later on, Lalo came over to take us shrimping. I went along just to hold the light. Dad didn't think he'd be very handy with the machete, but somehow he got six before we finally called it a night. This may not seem like very many shrimp, but they were so large that later when Mother cut them up, there was enough for a delicious shrimp and rice dish.

It was nine o'clock at night when we got back to the house, and Lalo would have to ride a couple of miles to get home. But what surprised me was that when I asked him if he wasn't afraid to go through the woods alone at night, he laughed at the idea. If there were any ferocious wild animals, they'd be twice as apt to attack a person at night as in the daytime, I thought. And realizing that he wasn't at all afraid, again I wondered if someone around the ranch wasn't purposely trying to scare me into staying close to home.

Señor Gomez was still stalling about letting me have a horse. I was sure now that he could let me ride one once in a while if he wanted to. Sometimes the *vaqueros* were sick or something, and their horses wouldn't get ridden at all for a week or more. Anyhow, the little I'd ride wouldn't hurt any horse.

And all that business about these horses not being safe . . . . Most of them were so overworked that they wouldn't move without being spurred. They didn't have energy enough to run away with anyone just for the fun of it.

I got another surprise a few days later when Lalo and Dad and I were passing the pigpens on the way to our swimming hole. There was the strangest smell in the air. It was like meat cooking—only different from the way most meat smells.

"What is it?" I asked Lalo.

He had an odd hangdog look when he answered,

Lalo

"The peons are cooking something for the hogs to eat."

"Cooking what?" I insisted.

He looked positively sheepish. Finally he said, "Meat."

"What kind of meat? It doesn't smell like beef," I said.

What he told me made me feel a little sick. But I wasn't as shocked as I might have been if I hadn't lived out in Texas cow country. The truth was that when the horses used by the *vaqueros* wore out, they were killed and their meat fed to the hogs.

In the United States we do what amounts to the same thing. There, old horses are slaughtered for dog food. I don't suppose it matters to a dead horse whether he's eaten by a dog or a pig. But suddenly, it occurred to me that instead of butchering it for the pigs, Señor Gomez might have given me one of the old horses to ride.

A few days later Mr. Ainsley flew in—without telling anyone he was coming. Dad was pleased because he had already fixed everything on the place that needed fixing, and he wanted to show Mr. Ainsley how much he had done. Dad's two biggest jobs had been to fix the big saw at the sawmill so that it wouldn't wobble and cut boards crooked, and to repair the electric power plant that ran all the ranch machinery and lighted the houses, too. I can't explain exactly what was the matter

123

with the electricity, but sometimes there was too much power and sometimes not enough; the plant had to be regulated so there would always be just the right amount of power.

Another thing he had fixed was a jeep with four-wheel drive that hadn't been running for a long time. Mr. Ainsley used the jeep to ride around the ranch and see how things were going—that is, when the jeep was running, which it usually wasn't.

Mr. Ainsley was the kind of man who is always in a hurry, rushing everywhere at top speed and not wanting to lose a minute. This trip he especially wanted to ride to a certain pasture where the next herd of cattle to be driven to the market was being kept. So the first thing he did after running his Cessna plane into its hangar was to look for Dad and ask what luck he'd had with fixing things. He figured Dad probably wouldn't have had all the tools he needed to work with, or all the right parts. But Dad knows how to weld—and well, he's a regular inventor anyhow. Mr. Ainsley said he thought it was "simply marvelous" that Dad had accomplished so much.

Dad told us all this when he came home for lunch. "Mr. Ainsley asked me to take him around in the jeep this afternoon," he concluded.

Of course Mother and I were happy for Dad. We

supposed it meant Dad had succeeded with his job where all the other men Mr. Ainsley had sent down had failed. Mother was especially glad because now it looked as though we'd surely be able to stay on the ranch. And I was thinking that if Mr. Ainsley was pleased with Dad's work—well, maybe I might ask him about a horse, since now it was clear that Señor Gomez wasn't ever going to let me have one.

I stayed home that afternoon because I thought maybe after their tour of the ranch Dad might bring Mr. Ainsley to our house, and that would be my chance to speak to him. Besides, my first correspondence lesson had arrived and I needed to study.

Actually Mother had been intending to ask Mr. Ainsley to have dinner with us. But that morning our maid, Flor, got word that her mother was very sick and she had to leave to take care of her. So Mother decided it would be better to wait until next time he came down. He always stayed at the *casa grande,* and generally ate there, too.

But when Dad walked into the house alone about four o'clock, Mother and I both knew from his face that something was wrong.

"What happened?" we both asked at once.

He was so upset that he couldn't even speak for a few moments. But after he'd flung himself down in a chair and kicked off his tall leather boots, he said, "It's the darnedest thing. I had that jeep running like a dream. Started it a dozen times. Drove it around. Couldn't have worked better. But the minute I got in it with Ainsley, it refused to start. I fussed and fussed until he said, 'Guess we'll have to walk around. You can work on it some other time.' Naturally, he didn't want to sit there all afternoon while I tinkered with it. Can't blame him for that. Of course, I offered to get our car. But it doesn't have four-wheel drive, so he said, 'Never mind; we'll skip it for this time.'

"Then I went to show him how smoothly the sawmill worked. The ranch carpenter was over at the mill making a cupboard for the *casa grande*. So Ainsley asked him to run through a log. And do you know, that carriage was loose again! Wobbled just the way it did before I fixed it."

"Do you think maybe someone tampered with things?" Mother asked.

"Who would do a thing like that? And why?" Dad replied irritably.

"Of course," he went on after a moment, "all machinery is ornery. Might be just happenstance."

"I'd surely hate to think anyone was deliberately trying to sabotage your work," Mother said.

"Well, at least the electric plant is working perfectly

now. Ainsley seemed really tickled when I explained what the trouble had been and how I regulated the power. He said no one else had ever been able to do anything about it. So at least we should have power we can depend on tonight."

It was dark by the time we ate dinner. And the electric lights came on strong and steady. But just as we finished eating, everything went black. Mother and I scrambled around looking for candles while Dad stalked out of the house with our big flashlight.

After we did the dishes by candlelight we sat out on the porch. We were both feeling awful, knowing how much more awful Daddy must be feeling.

There wasn't any moon, but the sky was very clear and the stars appeared unusually bright. Maybe it was to keep from worrying and saying other things that Mother began to point out some of the constellations to me. One of them was the Southern Cross, which I'd never seen before. Tonight all four stars shone plainly.

"How does it happen we've never seen it before?" I asked Mother.

"I guess because the sky is often cloudy in the early evening," she answered.

It was after midnight when Dad came home. He looked tired and beat.

"Was it a fuse?" Mother asked.

"If it had been a fuse I'd have had it fixed hours ago." He came as close to snapping as I ever heard him. "I rechecked everything I fixed. Everything was okay. Then I followed a line. Found a pole down; it threw the whole system out of order. Gomez—he went with me—said it might have been termites. They sometimes get into a pole. Or it might simply have rotted away. Pretty hard to tell at night. Have to wait till morning."

"What a homecoming for Ainsley!" Mother exclaimed.

"You can say that again," Dad answered.

After that we all went to bed—feeling like West Texans when a drought goes into its fortieth day.

11. A Visit from Ainsley

The first thing I did every morning was to go out on the porch and look at the mountains. Each time they looked different. Sometimes you'd think someone had hung a huge, dark blue curtain across the sky—but very unevenly. At times you could see all four ranges that gradually reached up to Chirripó, the highest peak, nearly thirteen thousand feet. Some days white clouds made the upper ridges appear snow-capped. Other days you could plainly see the dark green forests that carpeted the peaks and the lighter green patches on the lower slopes where the trees had been cleared away to make pastures.

Mystery on the Rancho Grande

What I'd come to realize was that mountain views are like sunsets, never twice alike, and forever changing. Instead of one mountain view we had hundreds and all of them lovely.

But next morning when I went out as usual to see my mountains, they had disappeared—completely blotted out by fog. What made it seem strange was that where we were the sun was shining and everything was bright and green.

Having my mountains disappear on me that morning seemed like the last straw. It was the first time since we'd come to Costa Rica that I felt blue. I almost wished myself back in Texas, going to school with all the kids—even if none of them knew where Costa Rica was. And I resolved to write letters to Evelyn Miller and Mary Kirby and some of the other girls soon.

When I went inside, Mother was making breakfast. She asked me to help because Flor hadn't returned from her mother's house yet. A few minutes later Dad made his appearance and we all sat down. But except for "pass the toast" or "butter" or "jam" none of us had anything to say.

Dad soon hurried off—with only half of his breakfast eaten. I helped Mother with the dishes and beds and then got out my books and started doing my lessons. It was the only thing I could think of to do that might make her feel more cheerful. I mean, to study without her having to prod me.

When Dad came home that noon he told us two men had been sent to the woods up near the *Camino Real* to cut down a tall guayacan tree—a species that termites hate like most kids hate spinach—to use for a new electric pole.

"Another man is already digging out the hole where the new pole will be set. This leaves the ranch so short of men that—" Dad turned to me, "—they've hired your young friend, Lalo, to help out. There's no way to get a truck up there, so they'll have to haul the pole out with oxen."

Later on I walked up the trail as far as my Seven Falls and sat down on a rock. They were getting the log from the forest where I had gone on my first day at the ranch, and I wanted to watch when the oxen dragged it across the river.

They had a special man on the ranch for driving oxen. He's called a *boyero*. But this time they were using two yokes, as they call ox teams. Lalo was helping the *boyero* because he's very good with oxen, as with all animals. Not everyone has the patience or knows how to handle them.

I had waited only a short time when they arrived. One yoke was hitched to the front end of the log, the

other to the back to keep it from rolling when they went down hill. They were enormous creatures, with long curved horns, one pair black-and-white spotted, the other a divinity-fudge white.

It was wonderful to watch how Lalo and the *boyero* maneuvered them across the stream. Both men were wearing rubber boots, and they waded across the ford with the oxen. I watched as the two teams slowly dragged the log up the ravine and out of sight.

That night when Dad came home to supper—he hadn't stopped work for lunch—the pole was in and we had lights again.

"What really happened to the old pole?" Mother asked. "Was it termites?"

"Termites with two legs," Dad muttered.

"You don't mean someone—?"

Dad cut Mother off. "I shouldn't say that. It might have rotted off below the ground. May have been a poor pole to begin with. But it looked as though someone had dug into the ground and had done some chopping, then threw some dirt back to hide the place. Of course, it could have been some animal gnawing. I have no way of knowing for sure."

Dad stopped, and I had a feeling neither of them wanted to say anything more in front of me. But that didn't stop me from doing some thinking on my own.

Later, he told us he had fixed the jeep again during lunchtime that day. The trouble was in the electrical connection. He had checked it out the day before and it had been all right. No one had used the jeep after he had fixed it. So what broke it?

After supper we all sat out on the porch. Though the electricity was working perfectly again now, no one felt like reading—or even talking very much. Dad had put his transistor radio on a table by his chair and was listening to the Voice of America. That's a program beamed from the United States to countries all over the world, and it's really good. They broadcast the news in "special English," which means they speak very slowly and clearly and don't use any big words so people just learning English can understand it. They also have music, including some good jazz, and a lot of different things. The program lasts from six in the evening until ten-thirty. But since we had to get up at five-thirty on most mornings, we hardly ever stayed up late enough to hear the whole program.

We hadn't been listening very long before we saw the jeep—the one Dad had fixed—drive up. And out popped Mr. Ainsley. Dad switched off the radio and invited him to join us on the porch. Mother brought out a dish of pineapple sherbet she had made that afternoon, and he declared it was the best sherbet he'd ever tasted.

A Visit from Ainsley

"That's probably because it's made with our fresh, sweet Costa Rican pineapples," Mother said.

Then Mr. Ainsley said to Dad, "I have to congratulate you on getting the electric plant functioning again. Having to chop down a tree, drag it three miles with ox teams, get it set, and the wires up all in one day . . . I doubt if it could have been done much quicker in the States, with all the paraphernalia they have."

"I had a lot of help," Dad replied.

"The jeep seems to run perfectly now, too," Mr. Ainsley continued. "By the way, what was the trouble?"

Dad repeated just what he'd told Mom and me.

"Sounds like dirty work somewhere," Mr. Ainsley said after a pause.

"I wouldn't want to accuse anyone." Dad frowned.

"I suppose not." Mr. Ainsley said this half to himself. "Well, maybe tomorrow morning we can take that jeep ride we had planned for this afternoon."

"Wouldn't you rather use horses?" Dad inquired. "There are so few places on this ranch that a person can get to by car. On horseback we might cover some parts you don't have a chance to see very often."

"I think you're right," Mr. Ainsley said. "Maybe next trip we can take an all-day ride around. But this time I have to start back by afternoon tomorrow. I have a couple of meetings to attend back in Texas."

They continued talking, and Mr. Ainsley accepted a refill of his sherbet dish. After a while, he got on the subject of the cattle on his ranch.

"I keep thinking this ranch is going to show a profit sooner or later. Then another year rolls by and I'm still in the red with it. Every year we send so many head of cattle to market. We weigh them up; they're driven down the *Camino Real* slowly and carefully, Señor Gomez assures me. But always when they get there, they have lost weight—sometimes as much as sixty pounds per head. And there goes our profit. Of course, you have to expect them to lose some, but to me that seems too much. After all, by the old *Camino Real* it's only twenty miles to the San Isidro market."

"Exactly how many head do you figure you have now?" Dad asked him.

"I wish I knew—for sure," Mr. Ainsley replied. "I get a report every month. It's supposed to tell me how many calves were born, and how many cows and steers we have, but I'm darned if I understand it. If you have two hundred cows, for instance, and each one has a calf, you'd think that would add up to four hundred, wouldn't you?"

"There are bound to be some losses," Dad said.

"Of course. But to my way of thinking there are just too many."

A Visit from Ainsley

"Maybe the pumas and jaguars catch some of them," I said, and right away everyone turned to look at me as though I'd said something real bad.

"What jaguars? What pumas or cougars, or whatever you call them?" Mr. Ainsley demanded.

"Well," I said, "everyone tells me the forests here are full of big wild animals."

Mr. Ainsley threw back his head with a snort. "You should try bringing a half-dozen of your friends down here on a hunting trip—the way I did after I first bought this place. In a whole week the lot of us only bagged one deer, two wild pigs, and a few birds. Oh, yes, the woods are full of them, they'll tell you. But just try and get within gun shot of anything."

They went on talking, but I didn't follow everything they said because I was busy wondering whether or not I dared ask about a horse.

One of the things Mr. Ainsley mentioned was how Señor Gomez was always hollering that they needed more pastures. But he—that is, Ainsley—didn't see why they needed more for the number of cattle they had.

"In any case," he said, "I want to get a lot more fields planted with jaragua grass."

Dad didn't know what jaragua was, so Mr. Ainsley explained, "That's a grass that's been imported from Africa. It's been found to grow very well here. Only difficulty is that the seed is hard to come by. I bought some in an agricultural store in San Isidro a couple of years ago and planted one big field with it. Gomez told me today he's found a farmer near here who is willing to sell me some more, but the price is awfully high. Still, I want to sow a lot more of it, so I guess I'll just have to pay his price."

I waited until there was a lull; then I said, "Mr. Ainsley, do you think—I mean, would you mind if I had a horse to ride once in a while?"

"You mean, they don't let you have a horse to ride?" he asked in surprise.

"No, sir. Señor Gomez says he hasn't any to spare right now."

"Nonsense," Mr. Ainsley cried. "They've got more horses than they know what to do with. Tell you what, you come over to the compound tomorrow morning with your Dad and I'll speak to Gomez. This is horse country. Everyone needs a horse here."

"Oh, Mr. Ainsley, thank you. Thanks ever so much!" I was so happy I hardly knew what else to say.

"The pleasure is all mine," he replied.

He left soon after that, and we all went to bed. But I was too excited to sleep. Every time I shut my eyes I could see myself galloping over the trails, up and down the hills, splashing through fords . . . .

12. La Brisa

I was out of bed early next morning and could hardly wait for seven o'clock. When Dad and I arrived at the compound Mr. Ainsley was standing talking to Señor Gomez. As soon as everyone had said *buenos días* to everyone else, Mr. Ainsley turned to Señor Gomez and said, "Isn't there an extra horse around here this little lady can have to ride? Ought to be gentle enough so she won't get hurt."

"Why, I think so!" From the way Señor Gomez said it, smiling and all, you'd think that he'd never thought up a new reason why I couldn't have one for each of the many times I'd already asked him.

139

"We've got a mare the men call *La Brisa*." (That means "The Breeze," only in Spanish it's pronounced as if it were spelled "Bree-sah.") "One of them was pointing her out to me yesterday," he continued. "She's fourteen years old now and not much good any more as a cowpony. But I think there's quite a lot of life in her yet. May have to rest her up a few days before you use her much."

"Chano," he called to a *vaquero* who was bringing a newborn calf down the lane past the compound. He was riding and holding the calf across the saddle in front of him. The mother was following, letting out a loud bellow every now and then.

Chano reined in his horse and waited at attention for Señor Gomez to speak.

"When you get to it," his boss told him, "put a halter on old Brisa for this young lady."

"With pleasure, Señor Gomez," Chano answered.

The *vaquero* rode on then to a small pasture behind one of the corrals where he dismounted and lifted the little wobbly calf to the ground.

"And you'll see that she has a place to pasture it," Ainsley told Gomez.

"To be sure," the foreman replied, as though nothing would give him greater pleasure. "She can use the pasture right next to her house."

La Brisa

As soon as Chano had finished putting down the calf, he rode into a nearby pasture where a number of horses were grazing. I climbed the corral fence to watch. After a short chase, he singled out a light gray mare, drove her into a corner and tossed his lasso over her head.

Once roped, La Brisa led easily enough. When Chano got her to the corral he dismounted and tied her to the fence. Then from the barn he brought a rope to make a halter-bridle. The Valley people hardly ever use bridles with bits. They just wind a rope around the horse's neck, behind the ears, and then around its nose, with a knot on each side of its head, just above the mouth. The two ends of the rope coming from the knots form the reins.

"There's your horse, Miss," Chano said, handing me the rope reins.

Up until then I had been so happy that I was finally going to have a horse that everything seemed wonderful. But one close look at this poor old nag and my heart sank.

"You call that a horse?" I exclaimed.

She was lame in one hind leg and her back was a mass of festering saddle sores. All her bones showed through her hide, especially the ribs. She looked as though she had been worked half to death.

141

Chano took off his hat and fanned his sweating face. His black hair had been plastered tight to his head by the *sombrero*. He was a Chiriqui Indian from a tribe down near the Panamanian border who have darker skins than most other Indians. His was the color of black coffee.

"She's not such a bad horse," he said. "Just needs a little time for the back to heal up." Then he picked up the lame foot to examine it. "Her foot will get well, too."

What surprised me when he examined her hoof was that the mare stood perfectly still although I wasn't really holding her. I figured horses didn't come any tamer.

"You get your papa to buy some grain for her, and you'll be surprised how fine she will look in two months," he said, as a faraway look came into his brown eyes. "I didn't like it when they said they were going to feed this mare to the pigs. I rode her when she was young. She ran like the wind. That is why we called her La Brisa. Once she saved my life. I started to dismount right on a big fer-de-lance, but she jumped away."

He patted the mare's neck. I began to feel a little better. At least I was glad that I had saved the poor old thing from being fed to the pigs.

142

Then Chano told me there was a veterinarian who came from San Isidro every other Wednesday to look after the cattle on the ranch. "Next time he comes, you can have him look at La Brisa. Maybe he'll give you some medicine for her back."

Chano didn't speak Spanish quite like the other people of the Valley. At first I couldn't think what the difference was, except that he spoke more slowly and seemed to be thinking to find the right words. Then it came to me that Spanish was not his native tongue. He was speaking it with an Indian accent, just as I was with a Yankee accent!

I led my horse home and tied her to a fence in the shade of a clump of young banana trees where she'd have some good grass to eat. Then I went into the house to tell Mother about my horse and also to ask if there was an old brush I might have to groom her.

It took Mother quite a while to find a brush I could use until we could buy a regular horse currycomb and brush, and by the time I got back outside, I found that my gray Brisa had nearly demolished the banana trees! They were young plants that hadn't started to bear fruit yet, and it had never occurred to me that a horse would eat them. I soon learned that they'll eat leaves, fruit, skins, and even the stalks.

I was sorry about the plants, but I was glad to know

144

how much she liked anything connected with bananas, because now I had something I could give her for a treat. Dad always kept us loaded with bananas. He would buy a whole stem of green ones which we would hang from a beam in the kitchen. Usually they ripened too fast for us to eat them all. But now, every time I went out to see La Brisa—which I did about every half-hour—I would take her a banana.

I soon found that I didn't need to keep her tied. Often, when she wasn't grazing, she'd come and stand by our gate as though she were waiting for me. No matter where she was, I could go right up to her and pet her anytime. Pretty soon she got so she would come when I whistled for her.

The *vaqueros* on the place could hardly believe their eyes—or ears—the first time they heard me call her and saw her come to me. They usually had an awful time rounding up a horse. Unless they could drive it into a corner where it had no place to escape, they'd have to chase it from one end of the field to the other before they could lasso it and drag it to the corral to saddle it. This was not because the *vaqueros* mistreated their horses; Costa Ricans as a rule are very good to all their animals. It was simply that the horses knew that being saddled usually meant a long hard day for them. The *vaqueros* had never seen a horse appear to like a person as La Brisa appeared to like me—or, if not me, the bananas I fed her.

When the veterinarian paid his next visit to the ranch, he gave me some medicine called Smear 62 to put on Brisa's saddle sores. It was an antiseptic mixed with some black gooey stuff to make it stay on. He noticed that she coughed, too, and he said this was because she had some kind of stomach parasites—one reason she was so thin. He gave me some medicine to put into her drinking water to cure her of them.

Her foot had gotten better of its own accord before he came. Now, using the medicines, it was marvelous how fast her sores began to clear up. And she was gaining weight, too. It looked as if I'd be able to put a saddle on her soon. That is, if I had one.

To buy a saddle, we'd have to go to San Isidro. But Daddy was very busy, and he didn't want to ask Señor Gomez for a day off so soon after arriving. Then we found out that all the stores in San Isidro were open on Sunday; that, in fact, Sunday is the big market day there when people from all the surrounding countryside come to town.

We left early the next Sunday morning; we'd already been on the ranch nearly a month and Mother had a long list of errands. It took us half an hour to get from our house to the highway, opening and shutting the gates and fording the rivers, and then nearly an hour more to get to San Isidro over the bumpy road.

We found San Isidro already full of people. There were horses tied all around the main square, and more people riding in from all directions. Some of the horses were brushed and curried to perfection and you could tell their owners wanted to show them off. Of course, there were lots of jeeps, too. But the funny thing was that although there were hundreds of people milling around, and children everywhere, there wasn't much noise. I decided that Costa Ricans are a lot quieter than Americans.

We arrived in time to attend eight o'clock mass in the San Isidro cathedral—quite a large, twin-towered church facing the square. Then we went to look at saddles. We were surprised to find how cheap they were—about a third of what they would cost in Texas. After looking at all the saddles in three shops, Daddy bought me a beautiful one in two shades of leather: the seat dark brown and the rest tan. It had all sorts of leather thongs and doodads hanging on it attached by silver-colored metal discs. Really fancy. Then he bought me a brush and currycomb.

"All we need now is a pad to go under the saddle," Daddy said.

Most of the pads were either bright yellow or bright

147

blue. I chose the blue because I thought it would look better with Brisa's gray color.

Afterwards we went shopping for Mother's foot-long list of groceries and household supplies. Then Daddy took us to a nice little restaurant where we had delicious chicken dinners.

I was really in seventh heaven when we finally bumpety-bumped home with our car piled full of all the stuff we'd bought. And my beautiful new western-style saddle sitting on top of everything.

My only problem now was getting Brisa's back well enough so I could begin to ride her.

13. *Along the* Camino Real

The first thing I did next morning—after gazing at the mountains—was to whistle for Brisa and examine her back. The sores had healed pretty well, but still I wasn't sure whether I should ride her yet. After all, I didn't want to make her back hurt the first time I got on her. I finally decided I should wait one more day.

But later on, while I was doing my lessons out on the porch, Lalo came riding up. He was on a beautiful black mare that belonged to his Dad—not one of the ranch cowponies.

"*Buenos días,*" we greeted each other after he'd tethered his horse.

149

Then I said, *"Pase, pase,"* which is Spanish for "Come on in."

He came up on the porch and said, "I promised to let you know when I saw an *oso.*"

"You've seen one? Where?" I was wild with excitement.

"In a tree by the river, in that woods where you went on your first day here."

"Can I see it?"

"Sure. I can take you there. But—is your horse all right now? I mean, it's quite a long way and it would be better to ride."

"Maybe you'll look at her and tell me what you think. I have a new saddle, you know."

"I heard you had. News travels fast on this ranch." He grinned. "Where is your horse?"

"Wait a minute," I said. I ran down to the gate, stuck two fingers in my mouth and gave a long, loud whistle.

You should have seen Lalo's eyes pop. I'm sure he'd never heard a girl whistle like that before. He was even more surprised when a minute later La Brisa came trotting up. And still more when she stood perfectly still while we examined her back.

"She's okay," he said. "The hair hasn't grown back yet over the scars but the skin is entirely healed."

150

Lalo tied her to the fence then while I ran in to get my tack and to let Mother know where I was going.

"That's a beautiful saddle," Lalo exclaimed as he came toward the porch to help me carry things.

He laid the saddle on the ground, then took the bright blue pad that went under it. But when he went to throw this over her back, she reared as though someone had stuck her with an icepick.

"Why, the pad can't hurt her that much!" I cried.

Lalo smiled. "It didn't hurt her. I shouldn't have swung it at her like that. She was just startled by the sudden movement of the bright color." He patted her neck to calm her down and this time slid the pad gently over her back. She trembled, but didn't jump or rear. "She'll get used to it," he said. When he put the saddle over it, she didn't seem to mind at all.

Next he slipped on her halter-bridle. A few minutes later we were on the trail leading past my Seven Falls, and through the big pasture where I'd had to be rescued that first day. The herd was grazing right near the trail, but now that I was on horseback the cattle paid no attention to me.

The trail through the woods—beyond where I'd been before—was rougher than anything I'd seen yet and I wondered how horses could pick their way among the many rocks. I believe horses not used to such trails would have stumbled or balked. But these horses, with their small, quick feet, seemed able to go anywhere.

"Our horses all have some Arabian blood," Lalo told me. "They're descendants of the horses brought over by the early Spaniards. That has given them about four hundred years to get used to this land."

Near the big river that cut through the woods, Lalo dismounted and tied his horse to a small tree. I got off, too, and tied La Brisa nearby while Lalo watched. He laughed at my knot and showed me how to make a slipknot that could be undone with one pull.

Then he led the way, walking toward the river. When we were almost on the bank he started looking up into the trees.

"Do you think it's still there?" I asked.

"It probably is. These ant bears are like sloths; they don't move around much. There are ant bears that live on the ground, but this kind spends most of the time in trees."

He kept looking. Then he said, "There it is. Can you see it?"

I craned and craned my neck, trying to make my eyes go where he was pointing, but the foliage was so dense that for a long while I couldn't see anything. Then suddenly, I did see it. It had thick, shaggy hair the color of unbleached muslin with darker markings along

152

its sides. It was sitting next to the trunk, its bushy tail curled around a branch and its funny long nose sniffing around.

"I wish it would move," I said after a while.

Lalo took a stick and whacked the trunk of the tree. This made the *oso* move first to a branch on the other side of the trunk, then into the branches of another tree.

"Could you keep one as a pet?" I asked.

"I guess you could," Lalo replied, "but you would be pretty busy hunting ants enough to feed it."

After we were tired of watching it, I asked Lalo, "What's on the other side of this woods?"

"Another pasture."

"And after that?"

"The *Camino Real.*"

"I've never seen it," I said. "Is it far?"

"No," he said, after a moment's hesitation.

"Let's ride to it."

Lalo looked a little reluctant, but he agreed as we walked back to the horses. We crossed the river at a place where it flattened out between two falls. Then we rode up such a steep hill I was almost afraid the saddle would slip backwards off the horse—and me with it, since I was hanging for dear life onto the pommel.

"Lean forward a little when you go uphill," Lalo suggested.

153

I did, and it made it easier for me and I think for the horse, too.

At the edge of the woods another wide pasture stretched before us. Lalo opened the Okie-style gate without dismounting—something I didn't imagine I'd ever be able to do.

"You know your way all over the ranch?" I asked.

"I ought to know this part," he said. "We live over there—just off the *Camino Real*. There, you can see the roof of our house sticking up above those orange trees." He pointed off to the left.

At the other side of the pasture a wooden gate opened onto a wide lane. "You mean, this is the famous *Camino Real?*" I asked, as Lalo held the gate open for me.

"That's it," he responded.

Grass grew along the sides, but in the middle there was a well-worn trail. Barbed-wire fences separated the *Camino* from the fields on either side, but in the place of fence posts, there were small trees—"living fence posts," Lalo called them. There are so many termites in the tropics that eat dead wood, he explained, that regular fence posts hardly last any time. Instead, they use live trees. Since it was spring most of the trees were in bloom. Some had lemon-colored flowers, others white or dainty pink ones, something like the blossoms on peach trees. You can imagine how lovely it was.

Along the Camino Real

"I guess it's the longest road in the world," Lalo said as he brought his horse up beside mine. "And it's still used. When Mr. Ainsley has cattle ready for market they are driven to San Isidro on this trail, instead of on the Inter-American highway. This way they aren't bothered by any automobiles."

"I can't imagine trying to drive a car over it," I said.

"It wasn't meant for cars, of course," Lalo explained. "Just horses and oxcarts. I guess in colonial days they kept it up a little better; maybe then it was possible to drive a carriage over it."

I tried to imagine what it must have been like in olden times—with conquistadores clanking along in their heavy armor and Spanish grandees in their powdered wigs and gold-embroidered jackets riding on their Arabian steeds. Just think—it went all the way from Peru to California!

"I'd like to ride a little way on it," I said.

"Why not?" Lalo answered, and led off to the right— the opposite direction from his home.

The trail was anything but smooth. There were streams and creeks and rivers to be crossed, and sometimes it was so rocky that our horses were practically stepping from boulder to boulder. Always there were woods along the larger streams, though between them were fields and pastures.

155

"Does Mr. Ainsley own the land on both sides of the *Camino Real?*" I asked. His ranch was beginning to seem bigger than ever to me now.

"Yes," said Lalo, waving his hand toward the mountains off to our left, "all the way to the top of the Talamancas."

Lalo was riding through the fords and up and down the sides of ravines just as though he were on smooth ground. But, though I didn't want him to know it, I began to get butterflies in my tummy every time we came to another river. Finally I said, "I think we should start back."

"Okay. As you wish," he said, turning his horse.

When we got back to the wooden gate where we had come out onto the *Camino Real* we were such a short distance from where he lived that I said, "Can't we go see your house?"

Such an odd expression passed over his face that I was almost sorry I had suggested it. I had a feeling he would rather not take me to his home. But why? Anyway, he evidently decided he couldn't say no, so he said, "Okay," and reined his horse in that direction.

The Ibarras lived in a two-story house. On the ground floor was the kitchen, and a place to keep tools and riding tack and things like that. The living and bedrooms were all above.

They had quite a large garden around the house, full of all sorts of plants and trees. There was a patch of pineapples, some bananas and papayas, and orange and lemon trees, coffee bushes, hibiscus and roses, and lots of other flowers I didn't know.

We went up a stairway that led from the ground floor to the balcony. Señora Ibarra had evidently seen us arriving and came out on the balcony to greet us. She was a very pretty woman, with a sweet smile and a lovely complexion. She seemed delighted to meet me. "Lalo has talked so much about you."

"I can't stay long," I told her.

"Long enough to drink a *refresco*," she said. And after inviting me to have a chair in their living room, she ran down to the kitchen.

I didn't sit down, though. Instead, Lalo and I stood out on the balcony where there was a gorgeous view of the mountains.

In almost no time Señora Ibarra was back with some delicious lemonade. After our ride it tasted good.

When we'd finished drinking it, I said, "I have to get home now. My mother will worry if I'm gone too long. I can ride back alone," I added, turning to Lalo.

"Oh, no," his mother said. "Eduardo will see you home."

"You might have trouble with the gates," Lalo added.

158

Along the Camino Real

I really would have been scared to ride back alone, but I hadn't wanted to admit it.

It was nearly lunch time when we got to my house.

"Lalo, why don't you wait here for your Dad and ride back home with him?" I said.

"No, no," he said quickly. "I'll go now. *Adiós.*" And right away he turned and started galloping back toward his home.

Didn't he want his father to see him at our house, I wondered? There was something about his behavior that I didn't understand.

Anyhow, I was so happy with my Brisa that I could hardly think of anything else for the next week, and I soon forgot about Lalo's sudden departure. I rode her every day—sometimes three or four times if Mother sent me on errands. I kept a saddle on her about half the time, and whenever Mother wanted something from the commissary I'd ride over after it. When she needed oranges I rode to the grove for a sackful. And, believe it or not, Brisa would stand absolutely still while I stood on her back to pick fruit from the high branches.

I was so happy, in fact, that I didn't notice that everyone else wasn't just as happy as I was—until one day when I arrived home quite late in the afternoon and found Dad sitting on the porch. Nothing unusual about that; he often sat there when he got home from work. Only this time when I said, "Hi, Daddy," he didn't answer with a "What have you been up to to-day?" or even with a "Hi."

When he didn't answer me, I took a second look at him. He looked tired and miserable and preoccupied. I went to find Mother, who was in the kitchen making a banana cream pie, and asked, "What's the matter with Dad?"

"Nothing," she said. Then, after a minute, she added, "It's just been one of those days."

"You mean when everything goes wrong?"

"Something like that."

"But what?" I asked.

"Run along now. Or go set the table."

I set the table. But all the while I was wondering what on earth had gone wrong.

Dad never uttered a word during dinner—until after he'd finished his first, though not last, piece of Mother's wonderful banana cream pie. I guess the pie must have mellowed him.

"I'm beginning to get the picture," he began. "Ainsley put Gomez in full charge of this huge ranch, and the authority has gone to his head. He's become like a little king. None of the people working here dares talk back to him or even make a suggestion. If one of them complained about something, Gomez would fire him and kick him and his family off the ranch. He's got a very good job—Ainsley pays him twice what most Costa Ricans would pay—and he doesn't intend to lose it, or have anyone interfering with the way he runs things. It's plain now why none of the other men Ainsley sent down here ever stayed more than three or four months."

"Do you feel he's trying to get rid of you?" Mother asked.

"He's the slick type. He'd never come right out and do anything you could accuse him of, but—"

"For instance?" Mother prodded him.

"Take the inventory business," Dad said. "You know how Ainsley is always wanting to know exactly how many cattle he has? Well, Gomez is making an inventory now. Today he sent me to a pasture that was over-the-hill-and-gone-from-nowhere to count the cattle in a certain field. He told me I could take one of the peons with me."

"Did you?" Mother asked when Dad paused again.

"Well, I assumed if he suggested it, he probably thought I'd need some help. And maybe it was a good thing I had someone with me who knew the way, or I might be there yet. It's easy to get lost on this place."

"You're telling me!" I blurted, without thinking.

At that, Dad turned toward me and said, "You be careful, young lady."

161

"I will," I said, sorry I hadn't kept my mouth shut.

"So?" Mother asked to get Dad back on the track.

"We spent all day going and coming, and hunting for what I expected would be a big herd of cattle."

"What did you find?" Mother, I could see, was getting as impatient as I was.

"There were exactly *sixteen* old cows in the pasture."

"Well?"

"Can't you see what a fool it makes me out to be!" I never heard Daddy sound quite so irritable. "I spend a whole day, take a peon with me, use two horses—all to count sixteen cows. As though I couldn't count up to sixteen all by myself."

"Maybe Gomez thought there were more cattle in that field?"

"Maybe. That's what I might have thought two months ago. But there have been just too many things of this sort. Remember how I had repaired everything on the place? And then, when Ainsley came, suddenly nothing was running?"

Mother nodded.

"I tried to believe then that it was just my bad luck. But now I'm beginning to wonder—not only about that, but about a lot more things."

Abruptly Father turned to me as though he had just remembered I was there. "You're not to breathe a word

162

of this to anyone. Do you understand that, Tamara?"

"I understand."

"It's my problem," he said.

"When is Mr. Ainsley coming again?" Mother asked.

"I think he's due in about a week."

"Couldn't you tell him—?"

Father frowned and said, "There's nothing to tell him. You can't just say you suspect someone; you have to have something to go on and I can't prove anything. Besides, even if I could, how do I know Ainsley would believe me? He's known Gomez much longer than me —I don't count when we were kids. He must have confidence in Gomez or he wouldn't have kept him all this time."

Just then I noticed Flor was standing by the kitchen door. We had finished eating. "I guess Flor wants to clear the table," I said to Mother.

"We're through," Mother spoke to Flor in Spanish. "Let's go out on the porch," she switched to English, "so she can get the dishes done."

We all left the table. And I probably would never have thought of the incident again—I mean about Flor's standing there by the kitchen door while we sat and talked—if it weren't for several things that happened after that.

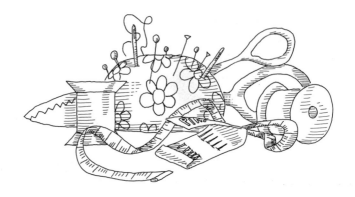

14. Snake in the Grass

The next morning after I got up I went out on the porch, as usual, to look at my beloved mountains. But there was a dense fog and not a mountain to be seen. It did seem that the mountains always disappeared just when I most needed them to lift my spirits.

I couldn't help feeling gloomy—especially knowing my folks were, too. Besides, I had begun to wonder what was the matter with Lalo. I hadn't seen him since that day we went to his home. His mother had been so nice I couldn't believe she had asked him not to see me. Did his father have something against me? Anyhow, that was the last time I had seen him. It would

164

soon be time for him to return to San José to school and then it would be months before he'd be back on the ranch.

The fog had made the air so sticky that I felt like going for a swim. But my folks wouldn't let me go to the river alone, and there was no one to go with me— Dad was at work, Flor was busy, and Mother, too. She was teaching English to some ranch kids two afternoons a week and helping some of the women with their sewing on other days, which meant she didn't have much spare time any more.

Later that morning when I was getting ready to go for a ride, Mother asked, "Where to today?"

"I thought I'd go up past my Seven Falls to the big woods and back."

"I'd rather you wouldn't go into the woods alone," she said.

"I won't," I told her.

And I didn't. I just rode to the edge of the woods and back. I was careful, as always, to shut all the gates, even though I had to dismount at each Okie gate to open and close it. I had hoped that I might run into Lalo along the way. But I didn't see him, or anyone else, either.

The next day when Dad came home for lunch he lit into me with, "Haven't you lived on a cattle ranch long enough to know how important it is to shut gates?"

I couldn't figure out what he was driving at, but I answered, "Why, yes, Daddy. And I do shut them."

"Gomez says you were seen riding past what you call your Seven Falls. Afterwards it was discovered that the gates on both sides of the river had been left open. During the night, the two herds of cattle got mixed up. It took three *vaqueros* half the morning to separate the herds and get them back into their own pastures."

"But, Dad," I cried, "I know I shut both gates. I remember because I had to dismount every time I came to a gate and lead Brisa through."

"Don't a lot of other people use that trail?" Mother asked.

"No one except ranch employees, and they've all been around here long enough to know the consequences of leaving gates open. Gomez has been known to fire a man for that."

Well, maybe you can imagine how awful I felt. For one thing, I was positive that I had shut both gates, going and coming. But who had told him I rode up that way—when I hadn't met a soul? I hadn't even mentioned to anyone except Mother that I was going in that direction, and Mother hadn't left the house or seen anyone that morning.

I was very upset. After thinking about it for a while,

Snake in the Grass

I decided the only thing to do was to go to Señor Gomez and ask him who had told him where I had gone. At the same time, I could tell him positively that I had not left any gates open, but I had no idea whether he would believe me or not.

Anyhow, that afternoon when Mother sent me to the commissary for some eggs and coffee, Señor Gomez was in the compound. I left Brisa at the fence and walked up to him.

"I'm awfully sorry you had so much trouble about the cattle getting mixed up this morning," I began. "But please believe me, Señor Gomez, I did not leave those gates open."

He didn't say anthing, so I went on: "What I'd like to know is who told you I was up that way yesterday."

This time he hesitated for a moment, and then he said, "I don't remember now who mentioned it. But you *were* up that way, weren't you?"

"Yes."

"Well, the gates were left open and it caused us a lot of extra work. But we'll forget it for this time. Just watch it in the future."

I knew he wouldn't forget it, but there was nothing more I could do. Somebody had told him I had ridden past the Seven Falls, and he was going to blame me for the open gates.

Mystery on the Rancho Grande

The next day was unusually warm. Toward noon the thermometer hit ninety—which is about as high as it ever gets in our part of the Valley. That is, at our altitude. I didn't feel much like riding because—well, where could I ride without being accused of leaving gates open or some other darn thing? If only I could go swimming!

Finally I asked Mother if Flor could go with me if I helped her finish the housework. Mother said yes. So I helped with lunch and cleaning up afterwards and we left about one o'clock.

Now, in all the time I'd been in Costa Rica, I had never seen a snake. But I always kept my eyes open for them, since I knew there are a few you need to meet only once. We were on the narrow path in the woods not far from the river. Flor was ahead—and paying no attention to where she stepped. I was a short distance behind her, because I'd stopped to look at a red flower with a bright blue center—such an odd flower that if you saw it in a vase you'd probably think it was artificial.

Then, all of a sudden, I saw a huge snake go slithering across the path between us. It was at least seven feet long, black and yellow with a small head and a tail like a whip. The middle part of it was almost triangular instead of round. And could it travel!

I didn't stop to think that there's no poisonous snake I'd ever heard of that fits this description. I simply let out a yell, "Snake! Flor! Snake! Run!"

In my excitement I completely forgot she didn't understand a word of English. But the strange part of it was that she started to run the instant I said, "Snake . . . run . . ." And she couldn't have seen the snake because she hadn't looked around. A second or two later, she stopped as though she suddenly remembered, and she turned just in time to see the long whiplike tail disappearing into the bushes.

"Do you know what kind it is?" I asked in Spanish.

"It's what we call a *mica*." (She pronounced it "meeka.") "They get awfully big, but they're not poisonous."

We went on to swim, and I tried to act the same as I always did. But it was something besides the cold mountain water that was making my heart beat about twice its regular speed. I began remembering things: how Flor hung around to clear the table the night Dad told us about the inventory; how she was the only person who could have heard me tell Mother where I was going riding that morning . . . .

Señor Gomez had been so very nice to send us a really competent maid. Could she be spying for him? I didn't know what to think. Or do. Should I tell Mother and Dad? Would they think I had been reading too many mystery stories?

I wasn't positive, of course, that she really did understand English. She might have started to run because I yelled. I'd like to find out for sure, I thought. But how? I probably couldn't take her by surprise again; she'd be on her guard now.

That night I thought and thought: how could I find

out if she knew English and had been spying on us all the time? I finally decided to play a little trick on her. That is, if she didn't know English it wouldn't be a trick. If she did . . . .

The next morning I rode over to the commissary to pick up our mail; it arrived about ten o'clock every day. There wasn't much—only one letter from Grandma Marquez for Mother.

"Was that all?" Mother asked when I handed it to her.

Flor was at the other end of the room folding up the spread Mother kept on the table between meals.

"No," I said in an extra loud and clear voice—the way the broadcasters give the news in "special English" on the Voice of America program. "Daddy had a letter from Mr. Ainsley. He says we can expect him down sometime tomorrow."

I was watching Flor's face as I said this. I was sure I saw her give a little start and her sharp, black eyes widen. But I just pretended I hadn't noticed anything and got a book and went out on the porch to read.

Not long after that, Flor told Mother we needed some more oranges and that she was going to fetch some from the grove.

When she came back half an hour later with a sack of oranges, she said she had met her younger sister on the way. Her sister had been coming to tell her that her grandmother—who lived about five miles away—was very ill and maybe dying, and that she'd have to leave early the next morning to go there.

I didn't say anything, of course, but I watched for Dad and when I saw him coming home for lunch I ran out to meet him.

Even before I had time to tell him how I had discovered Flor knew English, he said, "I hear I have a letter from Ainsley saying he'll be here tomorrow. Did you open it, or did Mother?"

He asked that because he and Mother as a rule never opened one another's letters.

"Who told you?" I asked.

"Señor Gomez said he heard it."

I knew then that Flor had understood what I'd said and had run to him with the news. But that didn't explain why she suddenly left whenever Mr. Ainsley came. Or was her grandmother—if she had one—really ill? I remembered how she suddenly left because her mother was sick the last time Mr. Ainsley came.

"Dad," I said, "walk a little way with me. I'll whistle for Brisa and we can pretend we're looking at her."

When we were farther out in the pasture I told him why I thought Flor was just pretending she didn't know English.

172

Snake in the Grass

Dad scratched his head and I was afraid he was going to say I was just imagining things. Instead, he said, "Once I mentioned to someone—I remember now, it was the ranch carpenter, Machero—that we had a very good maid named Flor working for us, and he said, 'Isn't that the girl Ainsley once took to Texas to work for his wife? She speaks English, doesn't she?' When I said 'No, she doesn't understand a word of English,' he said, 'Must be a different Flor.' I hadn't thought of the matter since."

La Brisa had come up now. I found a lump of *dulce* —that's a kind of brown sugar the Costa Ricans make by boiling down cane juice—in my jeans, and we stood petting her and fussing with her mane as we talked.

"Seems incredible that old Gomez would actually put a spy in our house," Dad said. Then after a pause, he added, "But it surely looks suspicious. From now on we'd better not discuss anything in Spanish or in English in front of her that she'd find worthwhile telling Gomez."

"And don't let on there was no letter," I said.

When we reached the house, Mother greeted him with, "I hear you have a letter from Mr. Ainsley?"

"Oh, yes. Yes." Dad began feeling first in one pocket, then another. "I thought I had it here; must have left it somewhere."

Later that evening, Dad had a chance to explain things to Mother. She listened to all we had to say, and then added, "No wonder she already knew how to run a washing machine and clean a refrigerator—when hardly anyone around here has such things."

Then Dad said, "I think the best thing we can do now is not to let Flor or anyone else know we are onto her."

"A man who would stoop to a thing like that would stoop to anything," Mother said.

"But now that we know what he's up to and he doesn't *know* we know it, we have a certain advantage," Dad replied.

I couldn't help smiling, thinking how surprised Señor Gomez would be when Mr. Ainsley didn't turn up the next day.

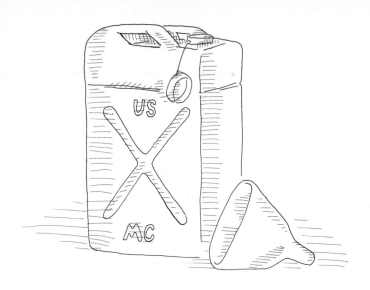

15. An Open Gate

The next morning we got up unusually early because Dad was supposed to go to San Isidro with Señor Gomez for the cattle weighing. It was during this dry season, when all the grass in the pastures was drying up, that the ranchers sold their cattle. Mr. Ainsley had left orders that every two weeks, beginning in January, fifty head of cattle were to be sent to market.

The *vaqueros,* headed by Pedro Ibarra, would start the day before and slowly drive them—with many rest stops on the way—along the *Camino Real* to San Isidro. The next morning, Señor Gomez would drive up in the jeep early enough to be at the weighing.

175

Mystery on the Rancho Grande

When Mr. Ainsley made his last visit, he told Dad
to go along with Gomez and to be present at the next
weighing. He was hoping, he said, that Dad might
discover why the cattle always lost so much weight
between the time they left the *finca* and arrived in
San Isidro.

Dad had arranged to accompany Gomez two weeks
ago, but it hadn't worked out. The nearest gas station
to the ranch was on the outskirts of San Isidro. Mr.
Ainsley had arranged for a gasoline company to deliver
a big drum of gasoline to the ranch around the first of
each month, but it happened to be near the end of
February and the drum was empty. Since both the
ranch jeep and our car were very low on gas, Señor
Gomez had suggested that he and Dad catch an early
bus that passed by on the Inter-American highway that
would get them to the market in time for the weighing.

Dad was to meet Señor Gomez in front of the commissary at five-thirty in the morning, but an hour and
a half later he had come back to the house fuming. He'd
waited and waited for Señor Gomez. Then, when it was
too late to catch the bus, a peon had come with a note
from Señor Gomez saying that he'd had to go to San
Isidro the day before and had stayed overnight. "It
won't be necessary for you to come," Gomez had said.
When he had read the note, Dad immediately started

our car, thinking he might have just enough gas to make the trip, but his gauge read nearly empty, so he had given it up.

This morning, so that there would be no slip-up, Dad had arranged to take his own car, telling Gomez that he wanted to do some errands afterwards. They had agreed to ride up together. When we were finished with breakfast, Dad kissed Mother good-bye and went out to start the car. But a minute later, he was back. This time, he discovered that the car had two flat tires! And was he mad!

Dad can change a tire mighty fast, but he was afraid Gomez would leave without him. So he told Mother he was going to walk over to the compound and tell Gomez they'd have to use the jeep after all. Then, since he didn't come back, we took it for granted that that's what they had done.

Flor must have left awfully early, because she was already gone by the time we got up. I helped Mother with the housework, but there really wasn't much to do since Daddy wouldn't be home for lunch. Soon I was free to do whatever I wanted. It was a beautiful morning. With Señor Gomez away in town I felt I could enjoy riding again, even if I only rode the length of the airstrip and back to my Seven Falls. It's a funny thing about riding: the more you ride the better you like it.

177

But it seemed to me I had never found it more thrilling than this morning. Brisa appeared to enjoy it as much as I did.

We tore down the side of the airstrip and back, then along the trail to the Seven Falls. This time, though, I decided I wasn't going to have anyone telling Señor Gomez that I had left gates open. So instead of taking La Brisa all the way to the river, I left her at the first Okie gate. I didn't even open it; I just slid under the fence at one side.

At the river I climbed out on my favorite rock and sat watching the water tumble and foam and bubble over the falls. I was still trying to figure out why Lalo never came by the house any more. Had I made him angry? Did he dislike me? Did his folks for some reason or other not want him to see me? Or what? He'd be going back to school soon, and if I didn't see him before then, I might never know what it was that caused him all of a sudden to stay away from me.

I hadn't been sitting there very long when I heard the creak of an oxcart—coming from the opposite side of the river.

"Well," I thought, "there's a witness that I left Brisa back in the pasture and didn't leave any gate open."

Just then the oxteam came in sight. It was the big divinity-fudge team, hitched to a fancy painted cart.

An Open Gate

Whatever was in the heaped-up cart was covered by a tarpaulin. The driver was on the far side, hidden by the huge oxen. It wasn't until the cart was right at the water's edge and the driver went around to the back of the cart that I saw it was Lalo!

He looked surprised when he saw me, but I thought he looked pleased, too. He hesitated for a minute as if he were uncertain about what to do. Then, leaving the oxen where they could get a drink, he came across the footbridge and hopped out onto a big boulder near the one I sat on.

"What are you doing? Where have you been keeping yourself?" I asked after we'd finished with the *buenos días* rigamarole, which the Latins never skip.

"I had a chance to work for a few days," he said slowly. "I'll be going back to school pretty soon, and my Dad can't send me very much money. I took this job to earn a little extra."

"That's fine," I said. "Lots of kids in the United States get jobs to help out, or to earn spending money." Then I asked, "What kind of work are you doing?"

"Hauling," he said, as though he were embarrassed or something.

"Hauling?" I asked. "Hauling what? What's in the cart?" The fact that he didn't answer right away made me doubly curious.

179

"Grass seed," he finally said, looking away from me.

"Oh. Jaragua?" I asked. He was obviously surprised that I would know what kind of grass seed he might be hauling, but I continued, "That's good. I know Mr. Ainsley has been wanting to buy some. He says it's the best grass for pasture. But he said it was going to cost him an awful lot."

Suddenly I remembered something. Once when our lawn in Dallas was in poor shape, Dad bought some grass seed to sow in the bare spots. The seeds were so

180

small that it only took a little package to reseed half our lawn. So I found myself exclaiming, "Wow. That's a lot of grass seed! It should be enough to seed the whole ranch!"

Lalo had a very odd look on his face, and he didn't answer for a minute. Finally, he said, "It's not threshed yet."

Then he slid back off his boulder and went to the side of the ford opposite the oxen. They were no longer drinking, and he gave the command—a sort of hissing

181

sound—for them to come toward him. That's an odd thing about oxen; you lead them more than you drive them.

I followed him and when the cart was close enough, I lifted the tarpaulin up a little and saw that the cart was filled with thousands of cut-off heads of grass.

"They have machinery for threshing it up at the compound," Lalo explained.

"If Mr. Ainsley wasn't in such a hurry for the seed, he could thresh some of his own grass and save a lot of money," I said. "Oh, well, I guess he knows what's best. Maybe he's decided it's more important to use his grass for pasture—to fatten up his cattle, so they'll weigh more in San Isidro."

As we were talking, I was patting one of the oxen and I noticed that it wasn't very sweaty. Oxen don't move very fast, but this yoke couldn't have come awfully far. "Where does the seed come from?" I asked, thinking how handy it was that the farmer lived nearby.

Lalo waved his hand in a vague way toward the mountains and said, "From . . . from up beyond the *Camino Real.*"

We stood there for a minute, and I guess neither of us could think of anything else to say. Finally I asked, "Aren't you going to have time to swim any more?"

"I hope so," he replied, "as soon as this job is finished.

An Open Gate

I'd like to swim a lot before I go back to school. I don't get much chance when I'm in San José. Anyhow, it's too cool for me up there." He paused, then after a moment added, "Well, so long."

"You'll see Brisa tied on the other side of the fence," I told him. "I'll be along pretty soon."

He gave the oxen a loud, short command and they began to move. A minute later they were pulling the cart up the steep incline out of the ravine.

After a little while I started home. I waved as I galloped past Lalo. There wasn't much point in trying to get Brisa to walk alongside of the cart, because at her slowest she was about two or three times as fast as the oxen.

When I got home I was astonished to find Dad was there. And Mother hurrying around to get some lunch on the table. He'd evidently just come in because he hadn't taken off his boots yet.

"How'd you get back so soon?" I asked.

"I didn't go," he said. I could see he was really in a mood.

"What happened?"

"Sit down. Lunch is ready," Mother put in.

"When Gomez saw me coming on foot this morning, he got in the jeep—before I'd even explained what had happened. I'm sure he knew about my tires being flat.

He probably sent someone over in the night to let the air out of them.

"He did the driving, of course," Dad went on. "I was the one who had to jump out every time to open and shut the gates. I was so mad it never occurred to me to look at the gas gauge—especially since I had filled the tank myself yesterday afternoon.

"Well," Dad continued, "we'd only gone about twelve miles when the engine died. I got out and looked to see what could be the matter. Finally Gomez said, 'Have you checked the gas?' Of course he's sitting there with the gauge right in front of him with the darnedest sneer on his face. Well, I checked for myself, and sure enough the tank was empty."

"There wasn't a leak in the tank?" Mother asked.

"Heck, no. Gomez knew all the time that we were out of gas—he'd probably siphoned off all but a half-gallon during the night. So there we were, halfway between the ranch and San Isidro, and not a gas station within fifteen miles. I was too furious to speak. I knew he'd planned it all to keep me from being present again when the cattle were weighed.

"Then Gomez said, as smooth as you please, 'We can't very well leave the jeep here unguarded. I'll catch the bus when it comes along, and you'd better stay here. I'll bring back some gas on my way home.'"

An Open Gate

"I don't know how you kept your temper," Mother said. "I'd have exploded."

"That wouldn't have done me any good. Anyway, I guess I was pretty lucky. I managed to borrow enough gas to get home from a lumber truck that happened to pass by. I'll bet Gomez will be surprised when he doesn't see me still stuck there on the highway. Still, I can't help but wonder what kind of stunt he'll try to pull when the next cattle drive is due."

"Maybe next time you can outfox him," Mother said.

"I doubt it." Dad shook his head. "A person who would pull that type of mean, petty tricks—his mind simply works differently. I'd never figure out what he was going to do next."

"He may overreach himself yet," Mother said consolingly.

Toward evening Flor returned. We all asked how her grandmother was. "Better, much better," she said—in Spanish, of course. But from the way she dived into her work you could tell she was uneasy and preferred not to talk about it.

The next morning after I finished my lessons, I decided I'd take another ride. But when I whistled for Brisa nothing happened. No horse. I walked out to a place where I could see all parts of the pasture, but Brisa simply wasn't there.

Mystery on the Rancho Grande

There was a gate at the far end of the pasture that opened into another field, and I ran toward it, wondering if she might somehow have gotten through it. I was really in a panic when I discovered the gate was partially open. At first I couldn't see any animals in that next field. Then, all of a sudden, I saw Señor Gomez and one of the *vaqueros* riding up out of a hollow. And driving La Brisa before them!

I figured I was in for it—even though I had never used that gate, so I couldn't have left it open. Now I opened it wider and stepped to one side until Brisa came up.

"Here, Brisa," I called. But she'd evidently been frightened and dashed right on through.

When Señor Gomez rode up he stopped his horse in front of me and, looking down from under his wide *sombrero*, said, "Well, *Señorita*, what have you to say for yourself?"

"*Cómo?*" I answered, which is like saying "What do you mean?"

"We found the gate open and your horse in the cow pasture on the other side."

"Señor Gomez," I said, although I could hardly get the words out, "I did not leave this gate open. I have never been near this gate before. I just came over here now because I couldn't find Brisa."

An Open Gate

Señor Gomez nearly always looked pleasant. I think he probably smiled even when he was ordering worn-out horses fed to the hogs. But just for a second he forgot to smile. And his face changed completely, as if he had been wearing a mask and all of a sudden it had dropped off. Without the mask he was the meanest, most cruel-looking man I had ever seen. He made me feel icy inside.

"This can't continue, you know," he said. "If Mr. Ainsley had been here and found your horse grazing in one of the cow pastures, he'd jump on me. It might even cost me my job."

I didn't believe that. What I did believe was that he suspected there had been no letter from Mr. Ainsley. We had played a trick on him yesterday, and now he was getting his revenge. He'd probably had somebody drive my horse into that cow pasture and leave the gate open on purpose. But I managed to keep my thoughts to myself, and instead I said, "It won't happen again, I promise you," though I could hardly speak.

"I want you to understand that this is your last chance," he went on. "If I find a gate open once more, or your horse out where it doesn't belong, I will get Mr. Ainsley's permission to take the mare away from you. Is that clear?"

"Yes, sir," I managed to choke out.

Mystery on the Rancho Grande

From the way he rode on with his head high in the air, you'd have thought he was some kind of lord or king and the *vaquero* and I merely two of his more lowly subjects.

The *vaquero* had closed the gate while Gomez was lecturing me. But after they were gone, I checked to make sure it was really shut. Then I started across the pasture toward Brisa. I was so angry that I could hardly see straight—things actually looked blurred.

Señor Gomez had never wanted me to have a horse—that was plain. Now he was determined to find a way to take her away from me. Why? What reason could he have for not wanting me to have a horse? What could it be—unless he was afraid that on a horse I might get around and see too much of what was happening on the *finca?* That could explain why he had sabotaged Dad's work on the jeep when Mr. Ainsley had wanted to ride around the ranch, too. And, of course, it explained why he had fixed it so Dad never got to the cattle weighings.

I had a small banana in my pocket. Brisa saw it as soon as I pulled it out, and she came toward me. I patted her nose and stroked her neck, then leaned my head against her mane. The next thing I knew I was crying. If my Brisa were taken away from me, what would become of her? Now that I had her in such tip-top condition, would she be given to some *vaquero* to be worked until once again she had almost no life left in her? And then, would what was left of her be fed to the pigs?

The thought made me positively sick. I took her gently by the loose skin underneath her jaw and led her toward the house. I knew then how much I loved her. I knew, too, I had to think of some way to prevent Señor Gomez from taking her away from me.

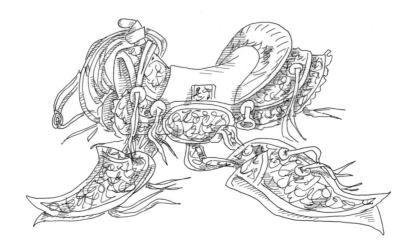

16. Lalo's Secret

I was so upset I hardly knew what to do. I hated to let Brisa out of my sight. I felt like getting on her back and just riding and riding and riding . . . .

I ran through the house to the back porch where I kept my saddle, stopping just long enough to grab up a scarf to tie down my hair. Mother was sitting by the living room window sewing. "I'm going for a little ride," I told her.

Brisa seemed to sense my mood as I turned her toward the Seven Falls. I hardly had to urge her at all. She dashed right through the water, then galloped up the rough steep hill out of the ravine. It's funny the way

190

horses often gallop up hills of their own accord—as though they want to get the difficult ascent over with as quickly as possible. In no time we were past the strip of woods that lined the river.

But when I dismounted to open the second Okie gate, I discovered that someone had tightened the wire loop that you have to slip over the gate pole. I pushed and pulled with all my might, but I couldn't budge it. I suspected that if I ever did get it open I would never be able to shut it again, but I was feeling so reckless that I didn't care. I was sure now that someone had purposely tightened the gate to keep me from going past that point.

Just then along came one of the very poor peons who occasionally got a day's work on the *finca*. He was barefooted, and from the looks of his short broad feet, I knew he'd never had a pair of shoes on in his life. His clothes were very worn and patched—there were even patches on the patches. Tied to his belt was a machete with a blade that reached to his ankles. He'd probably been chopping the weeds out of one of the pastures and was now on his way to report to Gomez.

He wasn't very tall, and like most of the peons in the Valley, he had very small hands. But a life of hard work had made him incredibly strong. I had often seen men like him wield a machete hour after hour where most American men would give up after ten minutes in a state of exhaustion.

"*Buenos días,*" I greeted him.

"*A Dios,*" he answered politely, separating the two words as though he were serious about commending me to God.

Then I told him, "I can't get this gate open."

He didn't answer. He just smiled, and with his small, powerful hands slipped the wire off as if it were nothing and held the gate open for me.

I jumped back up on Brisa, said "*Muchas gracias,*" and rode through. I looked back and saw that he had closed the gate after me. How I was going to open and shut it on my way home I didn't know, but for the moment I didn't care.

Brisa and I flew along—across the big pasture, into the forest, down the trail that dipped deep into a ravine, through the ford at the bottom, then up and into the next pasture. None of the other gates I encountered was difficult. I even managed the wooden gate that opened onto the *Camino Real* without dismounting.

On the *Camino* I turned to the right, the same direction Lalo and I had taken the day we had ridden here together. That first time I had been so intent upon the rocky, rutted, stream-cut trail and marveling that our horses didn't fall and break their necks (to say nothing

of our legs) that I had hardly glanced to right or left.
But now I held Brisa down to a walk and I could look
around a little more.

With its living fence posts on either side still in
bloom, the *Camino* was really beautiful. Some of the
trees had huge air plants hanging on them, many with
enormous red blooms. It was higher here than where
we lived, and the air felt fresh and cool. I was still
upset, but I began to calm down a little.

All this land, I was thinking, belongs to a man who
lives in Dallas, Texas, and he hardly ever sees it.
Dallas is a fine city, of course, if you like cities. But
who would want to live there, or in any city, if he
owned a place like this?

Just then I caught sight of the yoke of divinity-fudge-
colored oxen in a field on the far side of the *Camino*.
Their fancy painted yoke and enormous horns were
barely visible above the tall jaragua grass in the field.

Standing up in my stirrups I could see the painted
cart. And there was Lalo—busily cutting off the seed
heads from the grass and tossing them into the cart.

I slipped out of my saddle, tethered Brisa to the
fence, then pushed quietly toward Lalo through grass
as high or higher than my head.

I had expected to surprise him. But goodness! He
stared at me as though I were a ghost.

"How—how did you get here?" he stammered when he had recovered himself enough to speak.

"Rode. My horse is over there." I pointed toward the *Camino Real.*

"But the ga—?" He stopped suddenly, as if he realized he was saying something he shouldn't.

It was my turn to stare with surprise. "What about the gate?" I asked.

His face flushed scarlet underneath his deep tan. I waited, but he didn't answer.

"I found the wires so tight I couldn't open the gate. But while I was struggling with it, a peon came along and he opened it for me."

"But when you go back—?" Lalo had the oddest expression, worried and fearful at the same time.

"You mean the gate wires were tightened on purpose, so I couldn't ride up this way?"

Lalo kept his eyes glued to the toes of his boots, and I knew I'd hit the nail on the head.

"But why? Why?" I demanded. "There's no danger. That's all nonsense about these woods being full of wild animals, and you know it. Anyway, I'm on horseback, not on foot. Besides, the *Camino Real* is a public highway. I have a perfect right to ride on it."

He remained silent. But his face was a picture of misery.

Lalo's Secret

Then all of a sudden something hit me. I'd been so busy thinking about gates that I'd forgotten something else. When I remembered, I blurted, "Didn't you tell me when we rode along here that this land—this field—belongs to Mr. Ainsley?"

He didn't deny it. He just lowered his head again without answering.

"And that other load you were hauling, was that cut from here?"

Lalo couldn't look me in the face. I never saw anyone appear so unhappy. After a moment he slumped into the tall grass as though he could no longer stand up. I almost thought he was going to cry.

"Please, Tamara, please," he began to plead, "don't tell anyone—*anyone!*—that you saw me here today. Promise me. Please."

He looked so miserable that without thinking I said, "I promise, Lalo." With that I crouched down in the grass where no one could see me.

Suddenly, then, I began to laugh. In a way it struck me funny: Mr. Ainsley buying his own grass seed!

But a second later the laughter died in my throat, as another thought hit me—the idea that Lalo would do something dishonest.

"You knew this! And you're helping to cheat Mr. Ainsley!"

195

He put his hand to his forehead, half covering his eyes. "Please believe me," he begged. "I know it, but I'm not supposed to know it. I was just hired to cut and haul the seed. My father thinks I don't know it's being *sold* to Ainsley."

His throat was working as though there was a lump in it that he couldn't swallow.

"You don't know what it's like to work around here —for us, I mean," he went on. "Father has to do what Gomez tells him. If he complained or said anything, he'd be fired. He could never get another job that paid such good wages. Then I couldn't go back to school. I'd just be an ox driver or maybe a *vaquero* all my life. My father is a good man; I know he is honest . . . ."

"But why doesn't your father tell Mr. Ainsley?"

"He'd never believe him. He never believes anybody except Señor Gomez. Before my Dad worked here, there was another head *vaquero*. When they were branding calves, Gomez would always tell him not to brand certain ones. He knew Gomez was keeping these calves for himself, and he decided to tell Ainsley. Next thing he knew he was fired; Gomez accused him of purposely not branding the calves so he could steal them himself. Gomez is like that. He can twist things around and make Ainsley believe anything."

There were tears in Lalo's eyes, but he held them

back. "Please go," he begged, "before anyone sees you here. If you can't get the gate shut I'll shut it when I come through. We'll just hope no one passes before I can finish cutting this load and get down there."

"Can't I help you cut?" I asked.

"No. Without a knife you can do nothing. It's better you go—right away."

I did leave. But I knew I'd never forget the pain I saw in his eyes as he began to cut off grass heads again.

Going back, Brisa was true to her name, speeding over the *Camino Real,* through fields and woods. We hardly slackened until after we'd come out of the big forest and were crossing the pasture where I'd had to be rescued on my first day at the *finca.*

By then so many questions were swirling around in my head that I had to slow down to think. Lalo said he *knew* his father was really honest. But maybe he said that because he was trying to convince himself? How awful it must be to suspect your father is dishonest, I thought. I'm sure I'd be miserable if I found out my Dad would do anything as dishonest as selling Mr. Ainsley his own grass seed.

Then another thought came to me: Was this Pedro's idea? Or was he acting under orders from Gomez?

Of course I realized that a job as good as Pedro's— head *vaquero* on a big ranch owned by an American who paid higher wages than most Costa Ricans could afford—wasn't easy to find. If he quit, or said anything that would cause him to be fired, his son wouldn't be able to go back to school.

But even if Pedro were acting on orders from Gomez, how awful Lalo must feel to find out his father was doing such dirty, dishonest work to give him an education. No wonder he couldn't let his father—or anyone else—know that he knew. What else could he do but pretend he was merely cutting the seed for Mr. Ainsley and knew nothing about its being sold to him?

All at once, then, I began to realize what all this meant to my own Dad. I could see now that Gomez pulled every trick he knew to keep Ainsley from finding out what was going on, and that included keeping Dad in the dark, too. Just how many cattle were being driven to San Isidro every two weeks, for instance. Gomez might be selling a few extra—aside from falsifying their weights—to line his own pockets.

If Dad knew . . . .

Suddenly, I remembered my promise to Lalo: that I wouldn't tell anyone what I had found out today.

But I had to tell my folks! It wouldn't be right for me not to tell them. Dad needed to know what was happening in order to protect himself. He couldn't afford to lose his job either!

Lalo's Secret

What kind of a trap had I gotten myself into? I began to feel as though someone were tightening a noose around my neck. If I told on Lalo, his Dad might be tossed out with no job and no chance to provide an education for his son. If I didn't tell my Dad, he could be out with no job, no money, and four thousand miles from Texas!

By now I was nearing the tightened gate. I didn't know yet what I was going to do. Should I just sit there and wait until someone came along? Maybe no one would happen by before Lalo came along with his load. But more likely they would, because it was nearly noon. And if they found me on the far side of this gate they'd be apt to report it to Gomez.

Suddenly, anger broke over me like water over a dam. Gomez had no right to do this to me. No right to treat Dad as he was doing. And Lalo's father . . . .

But do you know, anger sometimes stirs up your mind, and all at once I had an idea. At the gate I dismounted. I tried once more to open it, but simply couldn't. Then I undid the rope that I use to tether Brisa, which is always kept coiled and tied to the saddle. I fastened one end of the rope to the pommel of my saddle and the other to the gate pole. After all, Brisa had been roping cattle all her life. She'd know enough to stand still and hold a rope taut.

199

Lalo's Secret

Costa Rican horses don't know anything about our whoas and giddaps. They only go by a rider's signals. So I got back in the saddle, then gave her a dig with my heels, at the same time lifting the reins and pressing tight with my knees. As I kicked her in the ribs I yanked off the scarf I was wearing and waved it over her head. She lunged forward, and held the position—just as though she were roping a steer—while I jumped to the ground, slipped off the wire and opened the gate.

I led her through, then repeated the operation on the other side. Again it took only a wave of my scarf to cause her to lunge forward, pulling the gate bar tight enough so that I could drop the wire back over it.

I patted Brisa's neck. I could have kissed her. A moment later I had recoiled the rope, tied it to the saddle and remounted.

"Where there's a will . . ." I found myself muttering that corny old saying out loud as we crossed the stretch of woods and splashed through the ford past my Seven Falls.

17. The Showdown

When I arrived home Dad was coming across Brisa's pasture from the compound.

"And where have you been off to?" He stopped to help me unsaddle.

"Oh, just for a little ride." I said it as casually as I could.

Mother came out on the porch then to tell us lunch was ready.

"Come on out and see our horse—how nice and sleek she's becoming," Dad called to her.

"I can see from here," she called back.

"Come out anyhow," Dad said more firmly.

202

The Showdown

She must have guessed there was some special reason Dad wanted her to join us. When she arrived outside the gate he said in a low voice, "Ainsley flew in this morning. I thought we won't mention it in front of the maid. Ainsley says he wants to talk with me. He's coming over shortly after three. If no one gets word to her, we may take her by surprise."

"What does Ainsley want to talk to you about?" Mother sounded worried.

"I don't know. He's having dinner this noon at the *casa grande*. When Gomez gets through telling him how I never got to San Isidro for the cattle weighings, how it took me and a helper a whole day to count sixteen cows, and how I don't even know enough to put gas in a car—heaven only knows what he'll say."

"Can't you tell him how things really are?" Mother asked, frowning.

Dad frowned too. "After Gomez gets first chance at his ears?"

Mother sighed.

"When we go in the house now, remember, we'll just be talking about the horse or the weather. No mention of Ainsley."

I stayed home that afternoon working on my lessons, or trying to. I was wondering if Señor Gomez would get a message to Flor.

Sure enough, about half-past two a peon appeared in back of the house. Two minutes later Flor, looking very agitated, rushed in to tell Mother she had to leave because her grandmother was worse.

Mother said, "Of course, if you must . . . ."

But as it happened, Flor had been cleaning and had on her oldest dress which was quite dirty. The Costa Ricans, like the Spanish, are very particular about their clothes when they are going somewhere. She simply couldn't go without taking a bath and changing her clothes and combing her hair.

Well, you never saw anyone hurry more, but she was too late. By the time she was ready to leave, along came Dad and Mr. Ainsley in the jeep. Flor tried to slip out the back door, but Ainsley spotted her.

"Hi, Flor," he called in English. "Come here. I've got something for you. Mrs. Ainsley wanted me to give you this." He fished a small package from his pocket. "A scarf, I guess. I didn't know if I'd get to see you or not . . . ."

Flor seemed glued in her tracks, but he went around the side of the house toward her. You'd have laughed to see the expression on her face.

"How are you? You're looking well," he continued. "Mrs. Ainsley wanted me to tell you she misses your candied yams."

204

The Showdown

By that time, Mr. Ainsley had reached the spot where she appeared to be taking root. He handed her the package which was wrapped in gold paper.

"*Gracias*," she finally said as though the word was half-stuck in her throat.

"You aren't forgetting your English, are you, Flor?" Ainsley asked.

She looked fit to be tied. Her eyes roved from me to Dad with the look of a trapped animal. When she didn't answer, Dad cleared his throat in such an obvious way that I wanted to laugh, and then he said, "Shall we go inside?"

Ainsley nodded. As he stepped up onto the porch, he said, "She was the best maid we ever had. You know, of course, that she's a younger sister of Señora Gomez?"

I saw Dad almost gasp at this information, but he managed to say, "Oh, er, yes—she's very efficient."

"How'd you happen to be so lucky?" Mr. Ainsley continued.

"Gomez sent her over to us the day we arrived."

I expected every minute that Dad would start telling Ainsley how the girl pretended not to know English and reported every word we said to Gomez, but no. He continued to act as though he hadn't noticed anything.

Mother met us at the front door, and after Mr. Ainsley had shaken hands with her, Dad asked him to sit down. Then Mother left to fix them some coffee, and Dad gave me a look that meant I'd better make myself scarce, too. I knew they had important things to discuss, so I went to my room.

I'm not usually an eavesdropper, but it would have been hard *not* to hear everything they said. You see, Costa Rican houses are built a special way. The walls are really just partitions and there's a big open space between them and the roof. This lets air circulate freely to keep the rooms cool even in the warmest weather. As it happened, there was conversation mixed with the air today, and I settled down to listen as closely as I could.

Mr. Ainsley began by telling Dad how disappointed he was with the way things were going on the ranch.

"The cattle situation seems to be getting worse instead of better," he said. "Frankly, I had hoped with you here that things would be different. But Gomez tells me you have failed each time to get to San Isidro for the weighing. And you haven't succeeded in checking the number of head on the ranch, either.

"Gomez keeps telling me we need more pastures," he went on. "I've been buying jaragua seed recently—Gomez discovered that he could get some from a farmer up above here—but it strikes me the price I'm paying is outlandishly high."

Then Dad spoke up. "What are you paying, if I might ask?"

I couldn't hear the price Ainsley gave, and anyway, it was in *colones* (that's Costa Rican money). An odd little silence followed, as though Dad might be figuring out how much that would be in dollars.

Suddenly, then, I found that for the first time in ages I was biting my fingernails. I'd had a lot of trouble breaking myself of that habit.

Next I heard Mr. Ainsley say, "Perhaps it was a mistake to buy this place. There are problems enough running a ranch efficiently in the States. But to run one in a foreign country where conditions are so different, where I have to depend on a foreman, and when I can only get down here three or four times a year . . . ." He paused and I could hear the sigh he heaved.

"The truth is," he continued, "I had hoped you would be able to take hold of things a little more. I don't know what's wrong, but you're the sixth man I've sent down here in the past three years. Each time it seems to turn out the same. Things get worse instead of better."

If Dad didn't say something for himself pretty soon, I didn't see how I could keep myself from dashing out and blurting everything I knew. But if I did, I'd never stop until I'd broken my promise to Lalo and told about the jaragua seed. At last I threw myself down on the

208

bed and covered my ears with my hands. Maybe if I couldn't hear what they were saying I would be able to keep my mouth shut.

As I lay there, I had a chance to do some thinking. Even if I did tell Ainsley what I knew, would he believe me? It would make him out such a fool that he might just decide I was mistaken. How many times I'd heard Dad say that people only believe what they want to believe.

But I couldn't keep my hands over my ears forever, and when I lifted them, Dad was speaking. He was telling Mr. Ainsley how it happened he had never arrived at San Isidro for the weighings, why he'd never made an inventory of the cattle, and lots more things, many that I didn't know anything about.

Then he told about the maid. How Flor had pretended not to know a word of English, all the while reporting to Gomez every word we said or move we made. And how she had always left when he was due to arrive, but got trapped this time. He mentioned that I was the one who had discovered she knew English.

"She's gone now," Mother said. She had just come in with the coffee and some pineapple upside-down cake. "And I'm willing to bet we never see her again—now that she knows she's been found out."

Ainsley said some nice things about how much he liked the cake and coffee. Then Mother said, "You'll excuse me; without a maid I have some chores to do." Afterwards I could hear her stirring around in the kitchen, and I figured she got out of the living room again so the men could talk.

There was silence for a while; I guess Dad and Mr. Ainsley were still eating cake and drinking coffee.

When Mr. Ainsley spoke again he sounded very solemn. "It's difficult for me, being so far away and unable to spend more time here. When I come down one person tells me this and another that. I must confess what Gomez tells me and what you tell me are very different, indeed. But you must realize that I've known Gomez for many years. He's the person I've come to rely on most."

Just what Dad had told Mother and me would happen: in a showdown he'd believe Gomez!

"I know you've come a long way to take this job," Ainsley went on. "I want to give you a fair chance. But unless things improve around here—say, within the next two months—well, I'll pay your expenses back to Texas and we'll call it a good try."

Hot tears were suddenly burning my eyes. I knew what this meant. In two months we'd start back to Texas poorer than ever. Mother would be sick with disappointment. And Daddy would never have a chance to justify himself.

All of a sudden I couldn't bear it any longer. I was going to give Mr. Ainsley an earful. I just couldn't keep still and let my Dad be blamed for all sorts of things that weren't his fault and be fired besides! Even if it did mean breaking my promise to Lalo.

I got up to open the bedroom door, but at the very moment I put my hand on the knob, I heard hoof beats outside. I glanced out the window and could hardly believe my eyes. There was Pedro Ibarra, stiffer and straighter in the saddle than I'd ever seen him before, heading across the pasture toward our house. Following him was Lalo, who looked as though he was about to be pushed off a cliff.

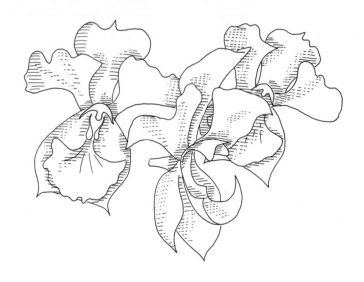

18. An Orchid from Lalo

Through the window I saw Pedro and Lalo tie their horses to the fence. Then I moved back so they wouldn't see me as they came toward the porch.

Dad was at the door before Pedro had a chance to knock. I knew by Dad's voice when he said, *"Pase, pase,"* that he was as surprised as I was by their visit.

I wanted to go out, but something told me I'd better stay where I was. Pedro and Lalo hadn't just come for a social call.

"I saw the jeep outside and thought you might be here," Pedro said after the customary handshakes and greetings.

An Orchid from Lalo

"You wanted to see me, Pedro?" Mr. Ainsley asked.

"Yes, sir."

Pedro cleared his throat. Then he began to talk as though he were repeating something he'd rehearsed over and over in his mind. "I want to explain why I am handing in my resignation."

"You're quitting?" Ainsley asked in a surprised voice.

"Yes, sir. Believe me, sir, it is not your fault. I—my job here has been very important to me. It has enabled me to send my son, Eduardo, to high school in San José. I had hoped he could go on to the University. He'd like to become a veterinarian. But I've decided it is better for him to remain ignorant than to build his future on dishonesty."

From the ring in Pedro's voice I could imagine he was standing with his back as rigidly straight as when he was on horseback. What he said must have given Ainsley a jolt, judging from the explosive way he cried, "*Cómo?*"

Then Pedro began telling everything that had been happening on the *finca*. How Gomez always sent three or four extra cattle to market that were never reported. How he falsified their weights by writing down the wrong amounts, and failed to record all the calves that were born. How he pocketed wages for peons who didn't work there at all. And all the dirty tricks he pulled to chase away everyone Ainsley sent down from the United States. The examples he gave included ruining the work Dad had done to fix the sawmill and chopping that electric light pole off below ground and blaming it on termites in order to throw the plant out of commission when Mr. Ainsley had visited earlier.

Pedro was talking a mile a minute now, and even with my ear pressed to the door I was having trouble following his Spanish. But suddenly my ears picked up the words *su hija* (your daughter) and *portón,* which means "gate." And I gathered he was telling Dad and Mr. Ainsley how Gomez accused me of leaving gates open.

"When he can't find any other means of driving a man away, he'll stoop to making life miserable for his family," Pedro said.

Dad started to say something then, but Pedro didn't give him a chance. "Now this grass seed. You must understand I have to do as I am ordered. Everyone has to. If Gomez even suspects you aren't 'loyal,' as he calls it, you are fired. But it's my son, Lalo—" His voice suddenly trembled as though he were going to break down.

"What do you mean about the grass seed?" Ainsley demanded.

Pedro cleared his throat again. "Gomez asked me to

get my son to cut it and haul it to the thresher. You understand, if I am obliged to do something dishonest in order to hold my job, that is one thing. But to drag my son into his schemes—"

He paused. He had begun to sound as though his throat were swelling shut with emotion and he could hardly speak.

"What about the grass seed? I'm paying too much for it, I'm sure." Ainsley's voice was rising.

"You shouldn't pay anything for it." Pedro finally blurted out. "It's your own seed!"

"What?" Ainsley fairly exploded.

Pedro went on to explain how at first he thought Lalo didn't know that the seed was being sold. Lalo had found out, but he hadn't said anything. "Now your daughter knows, too. She saw my son cutting it this morning."

"My—! Tamara!" Dad shouted to me, as though I were too far away to hear easily.

It didn't take me long to appear. If they guessed I had been listening I didn't care now.

"What's this about your knowing that the seed Mr. Ainsley was buying was his own grass seed?"

It was my turn to let go with an earful. I told Mr. Ainsley how Gomez made it appear that I left gates open as an excuse to take away my horse so I couldn't ride around and see what was going on. About how he let my horse out of its pasture and then blamed me. How he tightened the gate wires. And how I went anyhow and found Lalo cutting the grass seed heads on Ainsley's property.

"But why didn't you tell me?" Dad demanded.

"Yes, why?" Mother put in. She was standing in the doorway to the kitchen.

"I was afraid Lalo's father would be fired and then he couldn't go back to school and I knew how much he wanted to become a veterinarian. And anyway I promised I wouldn't."

"There'll be some firing around here," Ainsley declared. "But it won't be his Dad who'll be fired. But why on earth didn't someone tell me sooner what was going on?"

"Just to be seen talking to you alone would be enough to cause Gomez to fire a man," Pedro said. "Besides, when it was a question of a worker's word against his—"

The talk went on and on and *on*—for at least two more hours, with Pedro really letting his hair down about everything that was wrong or needed changing on the ranch.

It was only after it started to get dark that Pedro and Lalo rose to go. "We didn't bring our flashlights:

we should start back before it gets too dark," Señor Ibarra said.

After they had gone, Mr. Ainsley made me tell my story about the gates and how I discovered Flor knew English and about the grass seed all over again.

When I finished he said, "Lalo probably told his Dad that you knew about the seed. Then his Dad no doubt figured you'd tell your folks. That's what may have decided Pedro to make a clean breast of things, even if it meant losing his job."

"I didn't know what to do," I said. "I knew Lalo couldn't go back to school if his Dad was fired. And I knew how I'd hate to have my Dad lose his . . . ."

"You were in a tough spot," Mr. Ainsley said. "Well, young Lalo needn't worry about his education. We'll see that he gets to the University."

Pretty soon after that I left to help Mother in the kitchen. Mother had invited Mr. Ainsley to eat dinner with us, and he and Dad continued to talk in the living room while we got things ready.

At table Mr. Ainsley said, "Mrs. Perkins, how do you think you'll like living in *la casa grande?*"

That was the first we knew that Mr. Ainsley was thinking of promoting Dad to be ranch foreman.

"You know you'll have to put up with my dropping in on you for visits."

217

"I think I can put up with that all right," Mother laughed. "In fact, we think you should spend more time here. Do you know any other place as beautiful?"

"No, I don't think I do. And I'll make it my aim to come here more often," Mr. Ainsley agreed.

"And you, young lady," he turned to me, "maybe we owe this whole showdown to you. Tell you what, that horse you've been riding: from now on it's yours. Your very own horse. No one can take it away from you."

"Oh, Mr. Ainsley, thank you!" I didn't say it. I breathed it.

My very own horse! My darling Brisa! I was so happy I could have floated away on a cloud.

After dinner Mr. Ainsley and Dad went on talking in the living room. I couldn't hear what they said because I was washing dishes so Mother could sit with them. But I learned later that Mr. Ainsley had decided to give Gomez two weeks notice.

Within three days Gomez and his wife and Flor had all cleared out. "Maybe they were afraid if they stayed around any longer some more of their dirty tricks might come to light," Dad said.

In a way I felt kind of sorry for them—especially Señora Gomez. But in another way I thought Gomez was lucky that Mr. Ainsley didn't have him put in jail.

"It was partly Ainsley's fault, trying to run this big

place by remote control," Mother said. "It's so hard for the poorer people here to get ahead; Gomez simply saw his chance and took it."

"At least he left with his pockets filled," Dad remarked.

Two days later we moved into *la casa grande*. By that time Mother had a new *criada* to help her. And right away she wrote to Aunt Isabel to ask her if she and Uncle Pablo and Cristina and Eva couldn't drive down to visit us. And bring Grandma and Grandpa with them.

They came on the last weekend before school began. Dad and I rode out to the highway to meet them and lead them to the house along the same road on which the *vaquero* had led us when we first arrived at the *finca*.

We knew about what time to expect them, and didn't have to wait very long at the highway. Dad opened the big entrance gate and shut it after them, while I galloped ahead to the first river they'd have to ford.

When Uncle Pablo saw the river, he stopped the car just the way Dad had when he first came to it. Then I reined Brisa up by the car and said, "Maybe some of you would like to get out and walk across the bridge."

Cristina and Eva and Aunt Isabel got out of the car. Grandma and Grandpa started to follow, but by then Dad came up and told them, "Maybe you should stay in

the car. The river is low now and the crossing's not so bad."

Dad rode ahead to show Uncle Pablo the best spot to cross the river, while I tied Brisa to a tree and went over to the bridge to watch the fun. I knew exactly how my aunt and cousins felt when they saw that crazy swinging bridge high up over the rushing, roaring river. I had been scared the first time, but now it was hard for me to keep a straight face.

Cristina was the first to make it. Then I had Eva walk behind me and hang onto my belt and keep her eyes on my back. By that time Dad had crossed back to the other side and he helped Aunt Isabel across.

"It's your initiation to the ranch," we told them. But they'd been so scared they didn't find it very funny right then. Later on, though, we knew they'd laugh as they remembered it.

On Sunday we had a picnic down by our swimming hole. I invited Lalo to go with us too. When he rode up to *la casa grande* he had his saddle bags full of wild orchid plants that he gave me. One was a beautiful purple orchid—"a *Guaria morada*," he said, "our national flower."

"I never saw one before!" I said.

"They don't grow around here; only higher up in the mountains."

221

I guessed from the way he said it that he had ridden a long way to find it for me.

I left the orchids in the shade. Later I would put them up in some trees where they'd gradually fasten themselves onto the bark of the branches by their roots —which is how they grow naturally. Meanwhile Lalo unsaddled his horse and tied it where it could eat grass while we were gone. Then we all walked to the river, carrying our lunch baskets. We took along some folding chairs for Grandma and Grandpa.

Everyone, except Grandma and Grandpa, went in swimming. Aunt Isabel was too scared to ride down river on the current and she wouldn't let Cristina or Eva go out where the water was deep because they didn't swim well enough. They stayed near the edge where there was a sand bank and less current.

Lalo and I swam and swam for ever so long. Then we crawled out on some big boulders to sun ourselves while Mother and Aunt Isabel spread out the lunch things. Dad and Uncle Pablo were building a fire to warm up the coffee.

"You know I'm leaving tomorrow for San José," Lalo said. "Maybe you'll write to me?"

"Do you think you'll be able to read my Spanish?" Even while I asked it, I was resolving to work harder than ever to learn Spanish correctly.

"I'll manage," he smiled. "But I'll be taking English this year. I'll need it when I'm a veterinarian and will have to travel around to all the big cattle ranches owned by Americans down here. I hope some day I'll be able to write you in English."

I could see a red flush creeping over his face under his deep tan. I don't know why, but I think I was blushing, too. So I said, "Anyhow, I hope you'll graduate from the University in time to doctor Brisa when she starts getting old and ailing."

I think what I really meant was that I hoped we'd be staying in the Valley for a long, long time. With the care I was giving her, Brisa would live a long while yet. And I'd have years and years to ride her. Of course, later I'd have to go to high school in San José. But whenever I came home to the Valley she'd be waiting, ready to carry me across the fords, through the woods, and up and down our endless mountain trails.

Postscript

Yes, there really is a *Valle de El General*. Cut off by the Talamanca mountain range, the highest mountains in Central America, this valley remained almost uninhabited until opened up by the Inter-American highway some twenty to thirty years ago.

All the places described in the story exist. The author owns a small ranch in the Valley and has ridden horseback over many of the mountain trails and the *Camino Real*. She has also swum in the crystal clear rivers that flow down from the eleven to nearly thirteen thousand-foot mountain tops.

All the people in the story, however, are made up and are not to be mistaken for any actual inhabitants of the Valley.